WILLA

The Story of Willa Cather's Growing Up

WILLA

RUTH
FRANCHERE

Decorations by
Leonard
Weisgard

THOM   NY

To Hoyt and Julie

CHAPTER ONE

"WILLIE! Willie! Come on. Grandfather Cather's here," a small boy begged as he tugged at his sister's sleeve.

But the girl paid no attention to him. She bent over a big black dog that lay motionless on the rough wooden platform in front of the small railway station at Red Cloud, Nebraska. The light from the low-lying sun shone on her long red-brown curls.

"Willa! Daughter! Come now," her father called. Still she did not answer.

Beside Willa Cather, another girl knelt at the dog's

· 1 ·

head, stroking his sad-looking ears. Her full skirts were spread out around her and a brown fringed shawl covered her hair and hung down over her shoulders.

"Is he hurt?" Willa whispered, gently touching the forlorn creature's dusty, matted hair.

The other girl raised her eyes and smiled—a wide, friendly, reassuring smile. Just then the old dog rolled slowly onto his back and scratched it contentedly against the rough boards while he waved his limp paws. Both girls laughed, and soon their chatter filled the air.

Impatiently, Willa's brother Roscoe raced back to the family group around Grandfather William Cather. Besides Charles Cather and his wife Virginia Boak Cather there were their two boys—Roscoe, age six, and Douglas, age four. Their youngest child, baby Jessica, slept through the excitement, her head on Cousin Bess's shoulder. There was Grandma Boak, too, and Margie Anderson, the hired girl.

It was a large family that had alighted from the Burlington and Missouri train on this April evening in 1883. They had all come to live with Grandfather Cather where the dry air of Nebraska was healthful. Here Charles Cather would feel strong and well, just as his father did.

"Welcome! Welcome!" Grandfather exclaimed over and over, his usually stern eyes above his big white beard now shining with pleasure. "So you are glad to see your old grandfather," he said to Roscoe and Douglas, who clung to him. "All but my granddaughter Willa, who likes an old dog and an immigrant girl better."

He strode across the platform and took his nine-year-old granddaughter by the hand.

"So you like an old dog and an immigrant girl better than your grandfather," he repeated, his eyes twinkling. She was his favorite grandchild and she had not changed her independent ways since he had last seen her.

"Oh, no," Willa protested, squeezing his hand and looking up at him earnestly as he led her away. "But we were talking about our dogs. You see, she had a dog like Vic at home, and she had to leave him behind, too. I told her about Vic and she told me about her dog."

Grandfather stopped and looked sternly at his granddaughter. "Are you forgetting what the Good Book says about telling the truth, child? You know you couldn't understand that Bohemian immigrant girl. She can't speak English. None of them can when they first come here."

Willa nodded and then skipped along. "I know. She said some funny words. But I understood, just the same. I know about her dog and she knows about mine."

Next to the platform stood a huge farm wagon.

"It's so big!" Willa exclaimed, running ahead to examine it.

Grandfather laughed. "Everything's big out here. Big fields. Big sky. And you're a big family!"

The grownups climbed to the wide wagon seat, and the children scrambled over the sides and dropped down onto thick straw covered with buffalo skins. Boxes and trunks were loaded on at the rear, and still there was room to spare.

"Better settle down now," Grandfather said as the two big horses strained at their harnesses and the wheels squeaked under the heavy load. "We've a long way to go. It's sixteen miles to Catherton and home."

Roscoe and Douglas rolled on the coarse buffalo hides for a while; but soon they were asleep, for they were tired from the long train trip. Cousin Bess and Margie, the hired girl, curled up with baby Jessie between them.

But Willa did not want to sleep. She was excited, wide-awake. This was new country, and she wanted to see every bit of it. She hoisted herself up onto one of the trunks and looked all around.

About a mile from the station they passed through the little town of Red Cloud. Though the sun was gone now, Willa could see some people walking along the wooden sidewalks. Inside a few stores, lamps were already lighted. But very soon the village was behind them, and they were out in the country.

How different Nebraska was from Virginia, where they had always lived. All Willa could see was land stretching for miles in every direction. There were few trees here, no real hills, no fences—just the earth with its fresh carpet of early grass. It was the same to right and to left, and yet there was something exciting about it.

What was it that gave her this feeling of excitement? She looked inquiringly at the sky, so big and hard and far away. Stars were beginning to stand out bright and clear against the dark blue, and here and there small clouds scudded across them. In Virginia the sky had always seemed soft and near.

But there was something else. Suddenly she knew. It was the wind that blew from the southwest. It blew and blew without stopping—sometimes rising, sometimes sinking, but always there. It carried with it the smell of moist ground and growing grass and a faint perfume of blossoms. Wild plum blossoms, she thought. And it was exciting.

She took several deep breaths, and then ahead she heard the rumble of another wagon. Grandfather's team seemed to be overtaking it.

Willa scrambled to her knees on top the big trunk

and peered ahead into the dusk. They were approaching a small wagon drawn by only one horse. She could see that it was an old, rickety wagon and that the bony horse was tired and old, too. He hung his head and dragged his hoofs along.

Two men sat on the driver's seat and a woman and several children huddled together on the hard floor of the old wagon, surrounded by boxes and oilcloth bundles. The heads of the woman and girls were covered with shawls, and the men and boys wore strange-looking caps pulled down over their ears.

Suddenly, as the big wagon drew alongside, Willa recognized her friend—the girl on the railway platform.

"Hello! Hello there!" she cried.

The group of strangers, startled but silent, all turned their heads to stare at her.

And then "Ho!" the new girl answered, waving her hand happily. Willa could see that she was laughing.

"Willa!" her mother called back sharply. "They're perfect strangers! What are you thinking of?"

"Oh, no," Willa explained. "I know that girl. She had a dog and—"

Just then Jessie let out a long wail and four-year-old Douglas rolled over and began to whimper in his sleep.

"Sh!" said Bess. "For goodness sake, Willie. Be still now. See what you've done!"

Bess wasn't usually cross, but they had sat or curled up on the hard plush train seats day and night since they had left St. Louis, Missouri, and she was tired. Besides, sometimes she liked to let her cousins know that she was older, that she was almost a young lady.

"Lie down now, Daughter," Charles Cather said patiently, as if he knew just how she felt. "There will be more to look at tomorrow."

By this time they had passed the smaller wagon. Willa could see it jogging along behind. There really wasn't anything else to look at except the stars, and anyway she could see those easier lying on her back. So she slipped down onto one of the buffalo skins and stared up at the sky.

There, winking at her, was the Big Dipper. It was the same Big Dipper that she had looked at so many times back in Virginia as she sat on the steps in front of the big brick house or lay on the wide lawn at Willow Shade Farm. Yet she could hardly believe it was the same. They had traveled such a long way—nearly halfway across the country. She loved Willow Shade, but already she liked this new country. There would be new people to know and new things to do. And there was that new girl in the other wagon. Maybe she would live near Grandfather Cather's farm.

Willa began to think about the new girl with the big

brown eyes. Grandfather had called her "that Bohemian immigrant girl." What did that mean? she wondered. She started to ask her father, and then she remembered all the fuss she had caused before. Anyway, she could hardly keep her eyes open now. But she would remember to ask someone, maybe Grandmother Cather, the first thing in the morning.

CHAPTER TWO

FROM somewhere far, far below her, Willa seemed to be hearing voices. Was that Vic, whining and scratching at the door? She tried to call "Here, Vic," and struggled to open her eyes, but a bright light was shining directly into them.

She rolled over onto her face and smelled the familiar scent of clean, sweet bedcovers that had been stored with bags of lavender.

Suddenly she sat up, wide-awake. She knew where she was now! This was Grandmother Cather's house. The voices *were* from far, far below. And the bright sunlight was streaming in through a little window directly onto the pillow.

In a flash she was out of bed, throwing on her clothes helter-skelter.

"Come on, Bess," she cried to the sleeping figure in the other half of the bed. "Get up! We're here!"

Somehow, between the time last night when Willa had lain on the buffalo robe staring at the stars and this morning when she wakened beside Cousin Bess in a tiny attic room, the family had arrived at the farm and she had been put to bed. But now she was wide-awake.

She clattered down the narrow stairs, her shoelaces flying. But there was no one around; the voices were still below her. Down another flight of stairs she flew. What a strange house, where everyone was in the basement!

And there they all were, lined up on both sides of a long table, with Grandfather Cather seated solemnly at one end. Across the room, Grandmother Cather and Margie stood before a huge stove that was sending off the most delicious odors Willa had ever smelled.

The room was suddenly hushed; all heads were bowed. Father motioned Willa to a chair across from him just as Grandfather started to pray. She squirmed into place and stared at her plate while the firm, strong voice began to ask the blessing.

At first she tried to hold very still, but as the prayer

went on and on she cautiously raised her eyes. Directly before her was a huge platter of steaming corn bread. To the right was a great bowl of applesauce, just the way she liked it best, with cinnamon sprinkled lightly on the top. Her eyes roved on down the table to the pitchers of milk and big pats of sweet butter. Then over the bowed heads of Grandmother and Margie across the room, she spied two huge platters resting on the warming oven—heaped with sausage and ham and eggs. Were there griddlecakes, too?

Still Grandfather's voice went on.

All the others sat motionless, heads bowed, but Willa could not help staring at the great, crinkly white beard that kept tapping, tapping at the old man's chest as he opened and closed his mouth. It moved up and down, up and down, as though there were something alive under it.

She watched, fascinated, until finally she felt someone else watching her. She looked around cautiously and met her father's eyes. They seemed to have little crinkles in the corners, as though he were trying not to smile. And just as she was wondering about this, the long prayer of thanks was over.

Then suddenly everyone talked and passed things while Grandmother and Margie carried the platters of hot food to the table.

"Willa, you have *straw* in your hair. And *look* at your hands," her mother said sternly. "At least you must wash!"

Willa looked up beseechingly at her mother who sat, as usual, immaculately dressed, every hair in place. Even in the early morning, her mother always looked as though she were ready to receive callers.

Just then Grandmother came up behind Willa and started to heap her plate. "There's a washbasin behind the stove," she said quietly. "Hurry now, while I butter your corn bread for you."

Willa hurried. She brushed the straw from her hair as she ran and took a little of the train grime from her hands with a quick swish in warm water and a brisk rub on a towel. Then she was back at the table.

After breakfast everyone felt better. Father and Grandfather took the two boys with them to inspect the barn, Mother carried Jessie upstairs, and Margie and Grandma Boak cleared the table.

"Come, Willie," Grandmother Cather said affectionately. "We'll go out to the garden."

Willa followed Grandmother out the basement door and looked up at the house. What a different kind of house! It seemed to be built into the side of the hill, so that it looked tall at one end and short at the other. It was a plain wooden house, painted white, and much,

much smaller than Willow Shade, but already Willa liked it. It sat out in the sun and seemed warm and friendly.

With one hand Grandmother picked up a garden spade. With the other she took a stout cane from a nail by the back door and hooked it over her belt. The cane had a sharp spike in the end. Only crippled people carried canes, Willa thought, puzzled, and Grandmother Cather was straight and strong and well.

"What's that?" she asked.

"It's my rattlesnake cane," Grandmother answered, briskly leading the way down the path by the chicken shed. "I never go to the garden without it, and you must never go alone without a strong stick. Many a rattler I've killed, too. Just watch out and you'll be all right."

Rattlesnakes! Willa looked warily around, but there were none in sight. Soon she forgot about them as she gazed for miles across the fields. The wind was still blowing and blowing, but it felt good. The little clouds that raced across the sky told her that the wind must be even stronger up there.

But something puzzled her. Where were the neighbors? There had been some talk of them at breakfast, and she had expected to see houses on either side.

"Aren't there any neighbor children to play with?" she asked her grandmother.

"Neighbors? Oh my, yes. There are folks in all directions and more moving in all the time. A new family came last night, I hear."

Still Willa was puzzled. "But where are the houses?" she persisted. "I can't see any."

Grandmother laughed. "Oh, they all live in soddies. We're the only family, except your Uncle George and Auntie Frank, who have a real wooden house. That's because we've lived here the longest."

"Soddies?" Willa said the word slowly. She had never heard it before.

By this time they had reached the garden and Grandmother was already spading a new row for the pole beans that would soon have to be planted. But she left her work and stepped to the side of the garden where the wild grass had never been plowed. She set her spade in it and with her heavily booted foot drove the sharp edge straight down. It was hard work, Willa could see, but at last she had made a deep cut and spread the opening apart so that Willa could examine it.

"Look at that sod," Grandmother said proudly. "Grass has been growing on this land for thousands of years, and the sod of Nebraska is thick and very tough. People cut out big squares of it and make houses of them. They're warm in winter and cool in summer.

"Tomorrow we'll go over to see one," Grandmother

added when she saw Willa's interested face. "We must take some provisions to our new neighbors, the Sadileks. Poor things, they haven't any garden planted, and they can't speak any English, I suppose. They're immigrants —Bohemians."

"Bohemians!" Willa cried. "Oh, I know them. They're nice. There's a girl and she had a dog that she had to leave at home. She'll be lonesome. Oh, can I really go?"

Grandmother looked at Willa disapprovingly. "Yes, you can go, child. But you mustn't start making up stories on your very first day or I don't know what people will think of you. Come now and weed the new beets. We can't have idle hands when there are tasks to be done."

As Grandmother worked on down the long row, turning over the rich earth with her spade, Willa crawled along the row of beets and pulled the weeds from among the new red beet tops. While she worked she asked questions—all sorts of things that had come into her mind since she had first heard that they were to move to Nebraska. Grandmother tried to answer them all. Willa learned that there were no Indians or buffaloes around now, though there had been some only a few years before. She learned, too, that most of the neighbors were "foreigners," as Grandmother called them—families who had come from far across the water to try to farm the tough prairie soil. There were people from many different countries, and few of them could speak much English.

"But you'll have playmates," Grandmother assured her. "The Lambrechts live over there." She waved her spade off to the right. "They're from Germany, but they've learned to speak English quite well. There are two children about your age—a girl, Leedy, and her brother, Henry."

Grandmother laughed. "They'll answer all your questions," she said. "Your father warned me that you'd want to know everything all at once."

Willa began to grow tired of the weeding. She was sure her brothers, Roscoe and Douglas, were having a wonderful time with Grandfather. She sat lazily for a minute, thinking of the German children, Leedy and Henry, and the new Bohemian girl and wishing that she could be playing with them, when she saw something move along the garden row close enough to touch. It was brown, the color of the earth, but there were flashes of yellow as it slipped along.

Suddenly Willa was on her feet. "Oh!" she cried as she whirled around and snatched Grandmother's cane from her belt. "I'll get it," she shouted, brandishing the spiked cane over her head.

But Grandmother was quick, too. She caught Willa's arm and held it over her head while she shook with laughter.

"Oh, no—not Sam. He's my friend. You mustn't kill him."

"But you said—"

"Rattlesnakes, not bull snakes," Grandmother explained, taking the cane away from her granddaughter and hanging it again on her belt. "Bull snakes are fine to have in a garden. They eat the gophers and ground squirrels. I call that big one Sam. He waits out here for me every day—seems to know that I like to have him around."

And then when she saw Willa's disappointed face, she added, "But you were very brave. I won't worry about your going out alone any more. We'll go back to the house now, and later you can ask your grandfather just what a rattler looks like. I guess I've answered my share of questions for today."

CHAPTER THREE

THE next morning Willa wakened again with the bright April sun on her face. Voices floated up the stairs as they had the day before, but this morning there was no hurry to explore. She rolled over onto her back to stretch her stiff muscles and think about yesterday's wonderful surprise.

"Come, Willa," Grandfather had said after the noonday meal. "It's your turn to see the barn now."

He seemed solemn and stern as he pulled at his beard. Then she saw his eyes—such bright blue eyes with a twinkle in them. She was never afraid of her grandfather when she looked at his eyes, but she knew

· 18 ·

that other people sometimes were, because he prayed so long in such a grave voice.

The barn was very small compared with the huge one at Willow Shade. It was dark and cool inside, and quiet, too, for most of the animals were out in the pasture. Willa stopped just inside and laid her hand against the thick, cool wall. Suddenly she realized what it was made of—thick Nebraska sod, just as Grandmother had shown her!

And then she heard a whinny.

"All right, young fellow," Grandfather called. "She's here."

From the darkest corner of the barn he led an animal by a halter. Willa turned just as a wet nose nudged her. It was a pony—a sturdy little sorrel with white forelegs.

"Oh," Willa cried as Grandfather poured some oats into her hand, "he has *boots* on."

Grandfather threw back his head and laughed harder than Willa had ever heard him.

"Boots," he chortled at last. "I've been wondering what you'd name him. Well, Boots, how do you like your new mistress?"

Willa almost spilled the oats that she was holding out to the pony.

"You mean he's mine?" she gasped.

"Yours to ride whenever you like so long as you take

· 19 ·

good care of him," he said. "A Nebraska woman has to have a horse, you know."

All afternoon she had ridden her pony—around the garden, along the winding ravine that ran across the pasture land, and in and out of the bordering cottonwood trees that were just beginning to show their delicate green leaves.

Now, lying beside Cousin Bess in the snug little attic room, she recalled exactly how it had been the day before. From a fence rail she had slipped onto the sleek brown back of the little animal even while Grandfather was bringing out the saddle. And as though Boots knew just what they must do together before they would be set free, he circled the yard twice while Grandfather and the boys watched. Then, with a farewell flick of his tail, he was off in an amiable trot until they were out of sight.

The vast, new, exciting land lay all around. They could explore every foot of it together—know each hummock, each gully, each scrub ash. No one could stop them now! And no one did.

That was yesterday. Willa stretched again and was enjoying the pleasant pull on the muscles of her legs when suddenly she threw back the covers. How could she have forgotten for even a few minutes? Today she and Grandmother were to visit their new Bohemian neighbors, the Sadileks. There was no time to waste lying in bed!

Down in the kitchen, preparations were already well under way. Willa ate her breakfast close by, perched on a high stool so that she could see everything. In the bottom of a big basket went root vegetables from the storeroom—potatoes, carrots, dry onions. Then Grandmother sent Margie to the cave, a big underground room by the kitchen door, for a crock of butter and a slab of bacon.

At last, when they were almost ready to leave, Grandma Boak wrapped a loaf of warm bread and a pan of rolls in a fresh white cloth and laid them gently into a smaller basket.

"This is for you to take, Willie," she said. "Now mind you, be gentle with it, or the new folks will think your grandma wasn't the best cook in Winchester County, Virginia."

Grandmother Cather's gray mare and Boots were already saddled and waiting at the back door. Willa slipped an old cap from a hook near the washbasin and quickly shoved her tousled curls up under it before she lifted her basket from the table. But when she pushed open the door and saw Boots, she stamped her foot.

"I don't *want* a saddle," she said. "Boots doesn't like saddles."

"But Willie," Grandmother protested. "All ladies use saddles. In Nebraska we don't always ride side-saddle, but—"

"Then I won't be a lady. I'll be a boy. I don't *want* a saddle."

She jerked at the straps while Margie, the hired girl, always her ally, helped her.

"Hot old saddle," Margie muttered in her simple Virginia-mountain drawl. " 'Tain't right. 'Tain't right."

Soon they had it off while the two grandmothers stood by, protesting mildly. Freed from his burden, Boots whinnied in pleasure and flicked his tail. And before anyone else could stop her, Willa slipped onto his back, spread her skirt around her as best she could, and took the basket from Margie's helping hands.

Boots meekly followed the gray mare out of the yard and onto the wagon road that pointed back toward town. Then Grandmother took one worn rut and Willa the other, while their eyes roamed all about in search of fresh signs of the growing season. The warm days had sprouted the corn in the big field and brought tender shoots to the surface where they stood in neat rows criss-crossing each other. As Grandmother gazed at that field, peace and contentment replaced the annoyance on her face.

Gradually the two horses wound along the higher rough ground, avoiding the gulch that wandered back and forth without any apparent reason.

Willa sighted a windmill, but Grandmother shook her head. "No," she said. "That's the Lambrechts'. You can go there some other day."

On they jogged, following the crooked road until at last Grandmother pointed off toward the southeast.

"Look," she said.

Willa shaded her eyes and looked, but could see nothing.

"There in the clay bank," Grandmother persisted. "There's the place. And there are the children."

At last Willa saw two girls—one probably larger than she and one very small—standing in front of a crude sod hut that leaned against the side of a gully.

"There?" Willa exclaimed in disbelief.

Grandmother sighed. "Yes, poor dears. But they will build something more comfortable soon, I hope. Most of the immigrants who settle here are very industrious— and intelligent, too."

Willa kicked her heels against Boots's flanks. "Oh, I think it would be *fun* to live there," she called as her pony leaped forward.

"Be careful—the bread!" Grandmother gasped, clutching her own basket tightly as her startled mare tried to keep pace.

But Willa reached the doorstep well ahead of her, sliding off the pony and thrusting her jostled basket into the arms of her newest friend.

"Hello," she panted. "Grandmother and I have come to visit. I'm Willie. Willie Cather."

The new girl's eyes danced and sparkled as she watched Willa's lips. She tried the name slowly at first —"Wil-lie"—and then she laughed and tried it again, as though the very sound of it enhanced the pleasure of this second meeting. Finally, remembering, she pointed to herself and said, "Annie. Annie Sadilek," in a soft, liquid voice that made the name beautiful.

At this moment Grandmother drew up, and out of the doorway a woman emerged, blinking in the bright light. The little sister clung to her mother's skirt and hid behind her.

Grandmother seemed to know just what to do. She handed the basket to Annie's mother who took it with happy exclamations and placed it on the ground to examine its contents. All the time, the mother's voice flowed on, but here and there Willa heard enough words of English to understand how much their gifts meant.

"Good," she would say, "very nice—very nice," while she held up an onion or a carrot.

The bread brought tears to her dark eyes as she unwrapped it reverently and took the still warm loaf in her hands.

When at last Grandmother followed Mrs. Sadilek and her smallest child into the house, Annie and Willa were free to play. Annie raced around the beaten clay yard, down the gully toward the old windmill, and out across the field, pointing out everything in sight and asking the names. As soon as Willa realized what she wanted, the game moved even faster.

Annie would hold up a blade of grass or a stone. "What is?" she would demand, her brown eyes intensely eager in her pretty oval face, as though she must not lose a moment of this opportunity to find out all the things she did not know.

Willa would answer "grass" or "stone" and then Annie would try the word over and over, and on they would race, laughing and calling to each other.

Sometimes Annie would stamp her foot in annoyance, however, as she did when Willa called a very small and a very large stone by the same name.

"No! No!" she insisted. "Is not!"

Willa knelt down on the ground and thought. "Little

stone," she said, pointing to the one. "Big stone," she added, laying her hand on the largest one she could find. "Rock."

"Rock," Annie repeated. "Rock." And she was satisfied.

When they came back to the small shed near the house, Annie proudly gripped the handles of an old plow and pushed the blade into the earth. "Annie strong," she said. "Work hard." She raised her head and looked solemnly across the land as though she could see the corn that she would someday help to grow there.

By this time, Willa had played the word game long enough. Grandmother might come out at any moment and she still had not seen the inside of a soddie. She edged toward the open door until Annie took her hand and led her in.

At first, after the bright sunlight, she could see almost nothing except the square of thin paper at one side that served as a window. But she could hear her grandmother's voice and gradually her eyes became accustomed to the dimness.

Grandmother and Mrs. Sadilek were sitting in front of an old iron stove having what looked like tea. There was almost no furniture in the one small room—an old table and a few stools; a sort of bed in a corner, heaped with quilts and other bedding; a few boxes. Annie took her around to see everything.

"It's like a playhouse!" Willa exclaimed excitedly. She turned to her grandmother. "Isn't it, Grandmother? I'm going to try to make a little one."

Grandmother smiled. "It's harder work than you think—cutting the sod. But you can try."

All the while, Willa kept wondering where the other beds were, but she knew she shouldn't ask. There was a piece of burlap sacking hanging on the back wall, and finally, too curious to resist, she pointed to it. Annie lifted the corner to reveal a hole dug into the clay bank, like a deep shelf. There was a straw mattress on it—nothing more.

"Sleep," Annie said. "Sleep good."

As she looked, all Willa could think of was her own bed with its white sheets—the bed that she had jumped out of so quickly this morning, the bed that she had left for someone else to make up. She felt ashamed, and for once no words would come to her lips.

But just then a little brown head popped through the grass thatching above—a little striped head. Two beady little eyes stared at her—and then, with a chirping and rustling, the tiny animal was gone.

"A chipmunk!" Willa cried. "Oh, wasn't he cute?"

"Chip-munk!" Annie echoed. "Nice."

CHAPTER FOUR

THIS day with Grandmother was only the beginning for Willa. Each morning she and Boots would be off in one direction or another. Her small brothers, Roscoe and Douglas, were usually content with their own games. And everyone else round Grandfather's farm was so busy that no one paid much attention to her so long as she got back for evening prayers and supper. For the first time in her life she had the independence she wanted, and she made the most of it.

Often she rode over to see Annie, and sometimes she brought her home for a few hours—especially on rainy, dismal days when muddy water dripped through the sod house roof and dreariness settled over everything. But she soon understood that Annie meant what she had said about work. She was out in the fields early and late, laboring like a man. In a short time she took on an older, more serious look, and Willa realized with sadness that she was truly older than she had seemed that first day.

"Work hard," she would say when Willa asked her to play. "Help my papa."

One time tears came to her eyes. "Papa sick," she said in a low voice.

Willa felt a lump come into her own throat. She thought of the bewildered little man, Annie's father, who tried to work with his white, delicate hands but seemed weak and old. And then she remembered how she had felt when her own father had been sick the winter before they came west.

"Nebraska is good for sick people," she reassured Annie. "Your papa will get well."

Then Annie brushed the tears from her eyes and raced around the yard as she had that first day.

But most often, especially on the dry days when her friend was in the fields, Willa turned Boots's head toward the Lambrecht house, where Leedy and Henry lived. They had come from Germany, as Grandmother said, and had been on their land for several years. Everyone in the family talked and laughed a great deal, so that Willa loved to go there.

"Come in! Come in now," Mrs. Lambrecht cried from her kitchen door when Willa first rode up astride Boots. "Dis must be Villie Cadder! Oh, ve are so glad to see you. Come Leedy! Come Henry! Clara! Della! See who is come to visit!" She flapped her big kitchen apron up and down in excitement.

Willa looked up, delighted, into the rosy face and friendly eyes of the tall woman from another foreign country. It made no difference to these people, either, that she had never been farther away than Virginia or that she couldn't speak their language.

The children came crowding out then, a girl about ten years old in the lead. She had straight, sun-bleached hair anchored in tight braids that bobbed behind her ears. Her face was round and ruddy like her mother's and just as friendly. This was Lydia, whom everyone called Leedy.

Behind her was Henry, a little older, pretending he didn't care that she had come. But Willa could see that he did. He kept stroking Boots's nose and looking up at her slyly.

"Do you want a ride?" Willa asked, and his face lit up.

Willa handed the reins to him and followed the others into the kitchen, which was the heart of that house.

"Oh," she cried when she stepped inside. "This doesn't look like a soddie at all! You have real wooden floors."

"A cellar, too," Leedy said proudly while the whole family beamed. "Come see."

"And real windows," Willa went on as she followed Leedy to the cellar steps. "And a—a ceiling!" she gasped as she gazed up at the long strips of muslin cloth stretched overhead to keep the mud from dripping in.

Down in the cool cellar, Leedy showed her the bins for potatoes and pumpkins and squash, and the rows and rows of shelves for jars that the whole family would help to fill from their garden.

As she looked at everything, she kept thinking of the little sod house where Annie lived. Maybe someday the Sadileks could have a house like this where they could be warm and dry in winter and Annie's papa could get well.

"Mm-m-m—" Leedy said, sniffing the air above her. "Mama is baking something good. Mm-m-m— Come see." She led the way upstairs.

There in the center of the kitchen table lay a huge flat circle of hot coffee cake sprinkled all over with something crisp and golden brown and delicious-smelling.

"Mm-m—" Henry cried as he came inside. *"Streusel-kuchen!"*

"Streuselkuchen," Willa echoed, trying out the new word carefully so that she could remember it.

Mrs. Lambrecht set out cups for everyone, even the small girls, and poured steaming coffee from a great pot that had been standing at the back of the stove. It was a party! Even the little girls talked and asked questions of Willa.

At last, when most of the luscious, sweet bread had been eaten and there was a lull in the conversation, Mrs. Lambrecht looked at Willa hopefully and said, "You bring da mail, no?"

"Mail?" Willa questioned.

"From your grandpapa's post office. Sometimes da men bring it. Sometimes ve go—if da horses is not too tired." She sighed, and Willa knew that she was disappointed.

"No, but I'll find out about it. I can bring your mail every day!"

"Two times each veek," Mrs. Lambrecht explained. "Now da animals is tired at night, vorking in da fields all day."

And then she brightened, unwilling to spoil the happy time. "Come, Henry. Show Villie Cadder your rattles."

Bashfully, but willingly, too, Henry brought out a salt sack and proudly emptied the contents onto the table in front of Willa. It was just a pile of horny pieces or rings of something that she did not recognize.

She fingered them for a minute or two, turning them over to try to understand what they were.

"What *are* they?" she asked at last.

"Rattles," Henry answered proudly. "From rattlesnakes. I killed 'em myself."

"You killed all those rattlesnakes?"

"Well, you get more'n one rattle from a snake. Depends on how old he is. I've killed lots of 'em." He jumped to his feet and demonstrated with a great slashing of his arms just how he would attack.

"But I've been *looking* and *looking* and I haven't seen one yet!"

Henry explained that there were many on the wild land to the north and west and especially in what he called the dog-town, where hundreds of prairie dogs lived.

Before she left that day, Willa made Henry promise that he would take her there. He agreed that he would as soon as the corn was too high to cultivate. For the dog-town was too far away to reach on foot; he and Leedy would need a horse.

That night Willa found out about the little sod-house post office. It was called Catherton, was some distance away, and was beginning to be a real problem for Grandfather. Sometimes letters from foreign countries stayed there for days while he worried about them and yet was too busy to take them himself, especially during the spring and summer.

"Do you think you could deliver some of them, Willie?" he asked, rubbing his bald head with one hand and pulling at his beard with the other.

"I'd like to," she answered, trying not to show him how eager she was.

"Of course, young Virginia ladies don't usually deliver mail," he said with a twinkle in his eyes. "But you don't look much like a young lady these days. At least that's what your mother says when she tries to get the snarls out of your hair."

Willa tossed her curls back over her shoulders. "I *hate* long hair. Someday I'm just going to cut it off."

She looked down at the old, faded trousers that she had slashed off just above her ankles. "I hate skirts, too," she added. "Anyway, I'm not a Virginia lady. I'm a Nebraska girl. Everybody *does* something here. Please let me deliver the mail!"

And so, twice each week, she took a bag of letters, farm circulars, and newspapers (often in foreign languages) and set off across the prairie. Grandfather would give her general directions and describe the people in some way. Otto had a big red beard, he told her. Carl was a tall, sour-looking man, but his talkative wife and eight children would make up for his cheerlessness. Usually she could read the first names, though she seldom attempted the last names.

But she learned on her first day that she need not worry about missing anyone. Often before she had reached a dooryard, the whole family was out waiting for her—waiting for word from across the ocean, or just eager to see a new face.

In the Norwegian settlement, the whole mailbag was the subject of discussion. People sorted through it looking for something they were sure she had missed—or just looking. They would hold up a letter and chatter to each other in Norwegian mixed, out of politeness, with a little English. Ole had a letter from his brother, they would say, and wonder. Chris did not hear from his father—and whole families would worry. Then they would carefully bundle up the precious mail again before they would take her inside for "yust a bit" of whatever they had.

Maybe it was just some cakes made from corn, spread with molasses—or a bowl of rabbit stew. Into their rabbit stew, the Bohemians stirred dried mushrooms that they had brought across the ocean with them, giving it a different flavor that she learned to like. And once in a while, a Bohemian housewife, knowing that she would be coming by, saved a pan of warm *kolache*—little rolls filled with dried apricots or other fruit.

Delivering mail was like going from one picnic to another!

Meanwhile, Willa did not forget Henry's promise to take her to the dog-town. At every opportunity she reminded him of it, but it was late summer before they finally set out.

Henry and Leedy rode a huge gray horse, and Willa slowed her pace on Boots to match theirs. They circled by the sugar-cane patch, where Henry drew out his knife to cut cane for them. As they jogged along, he peeled pieces of it for each of the girls to chew. It was almost as good as candy, Willa decided, digging her teeth into the tough fibers to extract the sweet juice.

They took the old buffalo trail that at first wound along the creek and then shot off toward the north for a while, following the high places and avoiding the draws where water might stand after a rain. All along the trail, huge sunflowers nodded beside them.

"Folks say the Mormons planted 'em," Henry announced, proud of his knowledge.

"They wanted all the other Mormons to know which way to go," Leedy added. "The sunflowers showed them."

Boots contemptuously ripped off a great stalk of a giant plant and chewed on it slowly as he ambled along.

"Who were the Mormons?" Willa wanted to know.

"Oh, just some people that—that went west. Way out to Utah or someplace," Henry explained lamely, not sure, yet reluctant to show his ignorance.

The grass was tall at first, higher than their waists, and wine-red. But as they moved up the divide, farther and farther from the Republican River and the creeks, it became more sparse.

"We're getting closer now," Henry said. "Just watch."

"Watch for what?" Willa asked suspiciously. "I think you're just pretending there's a town for dogs, aren't you now?" She was never sure of Henry, for he was always playing tricks.

"You'll see," Henry answered mysteriously.

And before long she did see—a large area of several acres where the grass had been nibbled short.

Willa spurred her pony.

"Be careful! Snakes!" Henry warned, unable to keep up with her.

She pulled up in amazement when she reached the "town." Henry was right. It *did* look like a town. Hundreds of prairie dogs lived there in holes spaced as evenly as if someone had measured off the lots. Beside each hole was a little mound of earth that the animals had evidently carried up and deposited there. And in front of many of them, the little gray-brown dogs were sitting up on their hind legs, sunning themselves. They barked at her as she approached and then scurried down into their dark homes.

"Oh, aren't they funny?" she cried. "Why did they go?"

"You scared 'em, Willie," Leedy said. "They're awful afraid of everything."

Henry, fearing that his younger sister would spoil his story, burst in: "The owls live in their houses with them—just come a-flying right inside and make themselves at home." He made great swooping gestures with his arms and fluttering hands so that Willa could almost see how it would be.

"Snakes, too," Leedy added. "Snakes like to eat the owls' eggs and the baby dogs."

"Poor little things. Brrr," Willa shuddered as she poked with her stick at what seemed to be an abandoned hole. "Are they big holes?"

"Folks say they go *way* down in the ground to where there's water—just like a well."

Leedy scoffed. "Don't you believe it," she said.

"Let's try to see."

Willa and Henry attacked the hole with their sticks,

scratching furiously while dirt and feathers flew all around. They were bent over the hole, examining it and forgetting why they had come, when suddenly they heard a warning rattle. First Leedy screamed, and then Henry, as an ugly little head on a long, thin body struck.

Willa swung her stick wildly while Henry clutched at his arm, but the rattler slithered off into a hole before she could touch him. The horses neighed and shied— too late to warn them now.

"My knife. Get my knife," Henry moaned, while Leedy sobbed.

Willa pulled the knife from Henry's pocket and opened the blade. He grabbed it from her and slashed into the fiery spot until blood streamed from it.

"Home—home—" he groaned, clutching his arm to his stomach as though he were going to be sick.

Willa pushed him onto her pony's back, swung up behind him, and shouted to his sobbing sister to come on.

Boots seemed to know what to do. He raced as he never had before while Willa held onto the stricken boy. The galloping hoofs cut across the prairie, found the quickest route, and at last brought them in sight of the house.

In the yard, Henry's father was just carrying a bucket

of water from the pump. But when he saw the racing pony he dropped the bucket, threw up his arms, and ran to the chicken house. By the time Henry fell to the ground, his mother, pale and tight-lipped, was in the yard, too, the other children around her.

"Get da wagon," she commanded as she took a flapping rooster from her husband, wrung its neck with her powerful hands, and then tore a thick piece of meat from it. Willa saw great drops of perspiration standing on her forehead as she clasped the warm meat to the wound and bound it tight with her apron.

As though everyone in the family knew just what to do, Della held out a bottle that she had been holding, and the mother poured brown liquid into Henry's mouth.

The boy sputtered and choked and burst into tears for the first time. But he took a second gasping drink as though he knew that this was what he must do.

When the wagon pulled up, the mother lifted her son, tall as he was, and laid him onto the straw of the wagon bed.

"Liebchen, Liebchen," she uttered softly, and covered her face with her big, brown hands.

Then Willa knew at last what a rattlesnake was and what it meant to be bitten by one. She climbed over the side of the wagon and took Henry's head in her lap.

Most of the way in to town she shooed the flies away, mopped the perspiration from his face, and tried not to remember. The road seemed endless and she couldn't even look over the sides of the wagon. All the time, Mr. Lambrecht sat grimly urging the horses on—glancing back now and then at his only son, saying nothing.

At last when Henry seemed to sleep a little, Willa laid his head gently onto the straw and got to her knees. They were just coming into Red Cloud. This was Webster Street, she knew, and somewhere over one of the stores was Dr. Damerell's office. She thought of Grandfather's long prayers and hoped fervently that they had helped to keep the doctor in his office today.

As soon as the wagon stopped, the news flew through town. Everyone on the street and in the stores crowded around. Two men lifted Henry from the wagon bed and carried him hurriedly up the narrow steps. People shook their heads and talked about others who had been attacked this summer.

"Too bad," she heard someone say. "Just like the little Larson girl. Doc couldn't save her."

Nobody noticed Willa when she crept up the stairs. If Henry should die it would be her fault! She had made him take her to the dog-town.

Up in a small room, Henry lay on a brown leather couch, his head hanging to one side, while the doctor unwrapped the bloody arm and removed the chicken meat. He looked like someone else—not like Henry at all, Willa thought. Maybe he was dead!

The gray-haired doctor lifted a bottle from a shelf and poured white liquid over the wound. The strong odor struck Willa's nose and made her eyes water just as Henry let out a screech.

"What's that?" he howled.

The doctor chuckled. "Ammonia, my boy. Hurt as much as a snake bite?"

"Yah! Oh-h-h!!"

"Well, you're going to be all right now. You sound live enough to me, and you won't get any worse after all this time, so you'll just have to get better."

Then he chuckled again. "But tell your ma she'll have to let you sleep tomorrow. That was powerful snake-bite medicine she poured down your throat. Enough to make a grown man not mind getting bit."

CHAPTER FIVE

Soon Henry was well again, with only the scar on his arm to show to all who asked to see it. No one blamed Willa; instead, everyone praised her and Boots for bringing Henry home so quickly. In a few days, Mrs. Lambrecht baked another *Streuselkuchen,* this time with dried currants in it, as a special treat. After they finished the last crumb, Henry even played a few tunes for Willa on his harmonica.

But now the harvest and preserving season was on, and there was little chance for play. At the same time, Willa found another interest.

One evening when she was looking through Grandmother Cather's worn copy of *The Pilgrim's Progress,* she came upon a purple and gold pansy pressed between two pages. It was dry and brittle, as though it had been there for some time, but the colors and shapes of the blossom and leaves were still clear.

She carried the book to Grandmother Cather, who was sitting in her favorite rocker in the kitchen, mending.

"Who put a pansy in here?" Willa asked.

Grandmother laid down her needle and Grandma Boak dropped her knitting into her lap while she leaned forward to look, too. Margie Anderson, who had been setting the bread, came up between them, her hands covered with flour.

"Poor li'l pansy," she drawled. "All dead and dried up."

"Oh no, Margie," Grandmother said gently, knowing that the simple, kindhearted mountain girl often did not understand. "I put it away to keep it."

"Poor li'l dead flower," Margie continued as though she were looking at one of her pet chickens that a weasel had killed. She went back to her flour bin, shaking her head from side to side.

Willa sat down on the floor between her grandmothers. Sometimes if she asked the right questions in the evenings, she got a story. Roscoe, now nearly seven years old, slipped up beside her. He had been trying to make a rabbit trap, but it wouldn't seem to work right.

Grandmother's eyes took on a faraway look. "This is the first flower that bloomed for me after we came west," she said. "I brought the seeds from Virginia and never thought I'd raise a single plant. That was a terrible year; everything went wrong. First too much rain and cold, then a quick hot spell before we were ready. And oh, the wind!" she sighed and Willa thought she would never go on.

"The wind blew harder that year than I've ever known it to. It seemed to dry up the water faster than I could carry it from the new pump. But this flower came through, and I saved it so that I'd remember how good the Lord has been to us."

Willa knew that she was thinking other sad thoughts and so she changed the subject quickly.

"But how do you save them?" she asked.

Grandma Boak picked up her knitting again. "Why, Willie, I thought you knew. You just lay them out carefully between two pieces of paper and then put something real heavy on top, and don't touch them for a long time. They'll dry just as pretty as can be."

Willa sat thinking of all the lovely wild flowers that had come and gone this year while she rode thoughtlessly past them. She could have saved them, too, to remember. There had been yellow buttercups down by the horse pond in May and the wild plum blossoms— gone now until next spring!

"You could press some of my marigolds," Grandmother offered.

"Oh, no, I don't want old marigolds," Willa exclaimed impatiently. "They're not interesting. But I could get some goldenrod. Oh, dear, I wish I could save a sunflower."

"A sunflower!" Roscoe exclaimed and rolled over on the floor, laughing and holding his stomach.

The grandmothers laughed, too, and finally Willa saw how funny the idea was. There was *nothing* big enough to hold one of those.

"What's that purple stuff down by the shed?" Roscoe asked, afraid that he would be left out.

"Ironweed," Grandmother told him.

"I'll get you some first thing tomorrow, Willie," he promised.

"And wild roses!" Willa remembered. "I saw some yesterday. And snow-on-the-mountain! Oh, there are still lots of wild flowers. But we'll have to hurry."

"Well, just don't bring in any smartweed," Grandmother cautioned, "or you'll be sorry. If you get some of that in your eyes you'll think a rattler has bit you for sure."

The next morning Willa and Roscoe began their search for flowers. The first day they brought in all they could find, but most of them wilted before they could be pressed. After that they looked more carefully, selecting only choice blossoms and wrapping the stems in wet cloths.

They cut up most of the wrapping paper that Margie had been saving since April, and when the small supply of books for pressing was gone, they used every heavy object they could think of—even the iron cooking pots and the sadirons with which Grandma and Margie ironed the clothes every week.

Finally, one day, Margie could stand it no longer. She burst into tears and rushed back to her little room behind the kitchen. "Cain't even make my mush no more," she howled. "Took my sadirons and all my paper, and now my best kettle!" When Grandma got to her she was clutching the teakettle to her thin little chest.

"You come out now, Margie," Grandma said. "We'll find that kettle."

Willa was gone as usual, but the mush kettle, two irons, and six old horseshoes lined the wall of her bedroom, weighing down squares of brown paper.

Grandma put the irons into the kettle and handed them to Margie. "Here you are," she said determinedly. "She won't take them any more."

Margie lifted a corner of one of the papers. Under it was a spray of milkweed—flat and dry.

"Poor li'l thing," she mourned. But as soon as she clasped her arms around her mush kettle she was happy again.

As the days grew colder, Roscoe liked to stay near the stove, but Willa rode out as usual. Gradually the red grass began to take on a paler hue, the corn shocks grew dry and yellow, and the smartweed changed from delicate lavender to red-brown. Willa was always tempted to pick some, but she remembered what Grandmother had said. By this time she had almost completely forgotten about her old home in Virginia. Only a certain bark of a dog or perhaps the scent of drying hay would remind her for a moment.

She was a part of Nebraska, now, and Nebraska was a part of her. As she rode in the tall grass she seemed to move with it instead of through it. The wind rolled it into waves that rose and fell in constant motion; and there were times when she imagined herself on the ocean, sailing to some of the places she had heard of— Germany, Norway, and that wonderful Bohemia that Annie talked about. Those countries seemed to belong to Nebraska, too, if only she could ride far enough to see them.

But one frigid morning when Willa went outside,

everything had changed. Overnight the pale, late fall colors had disappeared. The whole landscape was one shade—a dull, leaden gray. She shuddered in spite of the woolen cap and mittens that Grandmother had made her wear. Everything's dead, she thought, surprised to see even a few chickens scratching and shivering outside the henhouse. She walked on down to the garden, but the sight of the blackened stalks standing limp and useless turned her away. At the horse trough she picked up a stick and slashed angrily at the thin film of ice on the water.

The flowers were all gone. The fun of riding over the land was ended until spring came again, months and months from now.

What could she do?

She could make a book of her pressed flowers, she thought listlessly. But somehow she didn't want to work on that today. She could read *Swiss Family Robinson* again—but she kept having to ask what some of the big words meant, and the boys would want her to read it to them, too. Usually she liked to read aloud, but not today.

And then she remembered something her father had said about going to Red Cloud this morning on business. She rushed back into the house.

"Where's Father?" she demanded.

"Gone to Red Cloud," Cousin Bess answered. "Shut the door, Willie. Don't you know it's cold?"

"Where's Mother?"

"Shh! She's upstairs. She's feeling poorly," Grandma Boak answered. "What ails you, child?"

Willa's face fell. "Oh, I don't know. Everything's different. I don't want it to change!"

Grandmother Cather looked out the high kitchen window at the leaden sky. "I know," she said. "I remember how I felt after the first killing frost. I didn't want it either—everything gray and black and frozen. But after a while I got used to it, and I've even grown to like it. It makes spring so welcome. Now, why don't you bundle up and go over to see Leedy? We'll start some lessons soon, but I'm too busy today."

It was after dark when Willa finally heard the wagon rattling along the rutted road. She threw open the kitchen door and rushed out just as it drew into the shaft of light, the horses breathing great clouds of vapor into the air.

As Father dropped stiffly to the ground she saw that the wagon was full of crates and boxes.

"I'll help," she cried, leaping over the side to drag a big bag of sugar from the top of the heap. "Oh, you've been to Miner's Store!"

"Careful, Daughter," her father cautioned. "Don't

rip a hole in that sack or Margie will set up a howl."

"And the hardware store, too!" she called. "You got a new ax handle!" She followed him into the kitchen with it and then out again for a box. Back and forth she went, talking and asking questions as though she hadn't seen him for a month.

At last everything was stacked in a corner of the kitchen, where the whole family had gathered. The table was set for supper, and the women were hustling hot food onto it. Mother came downstairs, too, a little pale.

Willa tugged at her father's long red muffler as he tried to unwind it from around his neck and chin. "You went to the drugstore, too, didn't you? There's a box of medicine and things. What else did you do? Were there lots of people?"

Father finally managed to unwind the muffler. He stood by the kitchen stove, rubbing his hands together while his family gathered round him. But Willa's questions went on and on.

"What's got into you, Daughter?" he asked at last. "I've gone to town once a month for supplies all spring and summer and you haven't even noticed. Now anybody'd think I'd been clear back to Virginia instead of to Red Cloud—even though that's a bad enough trip." He rubbed his tired back while he gave her a weary smile. "Every time I spend a whole day jogging in and back I wonder why they put the town so far away from us."

"Well, next time can I—"

"Hush now, Willie," her mother said sharply. "Can't you see how tired your father is? No more questions until after supper."

Willa took her usual place at the table across from Father, bowed her head for Grandfather's prayer, and then watched her father closely. He looked as though he had something on his mind. Sooner or later he'd begin to talk.

Grandmother's pumpkin pie seemed to revive him.

"Pie like that's almost worth driving sixteen miles home for," he said at last. "But I don't know how the horses felt about it on a raw night like this."

His wife's face brightened a little. "It must be nice to be in town in the winter," she said. "Is anything special going on?"

"Well now, let's see. . . . Doc Cook's put some extra shelves in the back of his drugstore. One of the traveling men sold him a new line of paints." He chuckled. "The ladies are taking up china painting, he says. Putting decorations on all their plates and cups."

Willa's mother looked interested.

"And everybody's talking about plans for a new

opera house. The old one is too small. Trouble is, they can't agree on where it ought to be."

"Opera house?" Willa couldn't hold in any longer. "What for?"

"For all the entertainments. Seems they're going to have quite a few this winter."

He reached into his pocket and brought out a handbill. Everyone crowded around him to look while he read aloud: "The Management is pleased to present that Great Drama of Human Suffering and Revenge, *The Count of Monte Cristo,* on Saturday Evening, the first of December."

"And here's a list of all the players," he added.

"A real count! Right here in Nebraska? Maybe he's from Bohemia! Annie says—"

"Oh, hush, Willie. Of course it isn't a real count," Cousin Bess explained impatiently. "It's a *play,* with real actors and actresses, maybe from New York or some place like that."

Willa almost pulled her father's chair over. "Let's go. Let's *all* go! We can, can't we?"

There was a breathless silence while all eyes were fixed on Father.

Slowly he shook his head. "I'm afraid not," he answered sadly. "I—I guess I shouldn't have brought that handbill home—didn't realize you'd all get so excited.

You see, it's at night and not until next month—December. Why, we could all be snowed in by that time. It's a bitter-cold drive, I can tell you. No, we can't go."

"Well, maybe we could move to Red Cloud for the winter," Willa persisted, still hopeful.

Her mother sighed. "It *would* be nice, Charles. I worry about being so far from a doctor. And there's the children's education to think of. Besides, there are just too many of us here."

Father got to his feet wearily.

"Well, I can't solve this problem tonight just because the Count of Monte Cristo is coming to town. But if it will make you feel better, Daughter, you can have this." He handed her the folded handbill.

"And tomorrow I'll try to tell you what the play is about."

Willa took the paper from him and slowly climbed the dark stairs to her room. Already her mind was at work. Maybe tomorrow Leedy and Annie could come over. They could have a play. She could be the Count of Monte Cristo. She would suffer and have her revenge!

CHAPTER SIX

NEARLY a year went by, however, before the family finally moved to Red Cloud. It was a year of uncertainty, with many discussions around the stove in the evenings. Mother was sure that farm life was too hard for her husband. Cousin Bess wanted to meet more young people. And when the new baby boy, Jim, arrived, there just didn't seem to be any place to put him.

Willa wasn't sure how she felt. Some days during the long winter she wanted to go, especially when someone brought news from town. But then there were other times—like the times when Margie made popcorn in the evening and brought crisp red apples from the store-room, and they all sat around to hear Grandmother read one of William Shakespeare's exciting plays or her favorite *The Pilgrim's Progress*. Or maybe a warm, high wind would blow and remind her of the wonderful summer. Then Willa thought she would rather stay.

Spring, so fruitful that first year, was late; but when the wild grass finally sprouted thick and green, Willa took to the old buffalo trails again with her bag of mail. There were still a few places she hadn't seen—the French settlement, almost a little separate country, with its colorful church and gay celebrations; some new homesteaders here and there; more ground being broken for sod corn.

"You'll come back to visit every summer," Grandfather said one morning as he filled the horse trough with fresh water. "Everybody'll be right glad to see you. And when you move into Red Cloud, all your friends will have a place to stop over. They'll like that."

Willa could tell then by the way he looked that it was all settled. They were going to move. She felt her throat go dry and for a minute she was afraid she was going to cry, just as if she were still only nine years old instead of going on eleven and big for her age.

She leaned against the old windmill and looked far up into it.

"Someday I'm going to climb clear to the top," she said determinedly. "Maybe I could see all of Nebraska from there."

Grandfather chuckled. "Well, just be sure that you can get down again. I'm too old to climb up after you."

So they packed up everything they owned, and one September morning they stowed it in the rear of the big wagon and began the trip back to Red Cloud. How different from that first trip, Willa thought, as she sat on the same trunk and kicked her heels against it. Everyone was clean and rested instead of tired and dirty and covered with train soot. No one told her to hush—at least, not for a long time. The grass was tall and red now; no wild plum blossoms perfumed the wind. But even though she knew every scent and sight along the road, she was still excited. No matter *how* much she liked Red Cloud, she would never forget the farm and her friends from many countries. She would go back as often as she could.

As they finally came into the town, everyone stirred from a warm drowsiness. Even baby Jim seemed to want to see, and Jessie tried to pull her chin up above one side of the wagon while the boys crowded to the other. Down Webster Street they rolled, past a few straggling frame houses.

"What's that?" Roscoe called, pointing across an

open space to an imposing brick building set in the middle of a block of trees.

"The Webster County Court House," his father answered, "where they keep all the records."

"What're records?" Douglas wanted to know as he balanced on top of a wobbly box.

But before Father could answer there were other things to see. They passed a number of small stores.

"What's that?" Willa cried, pointing to a large building on a corner where workmen were carrying bricks up a ladder.

"They finally decided to build the opera house there, above the hardware store," Grandfather replied over his shoulder. "I hope they don't start having any sinful things going on there."

"The opera house!" Willa had almost forgotten about it, but here it was at last. Only what if she wouldn't be allowed to go there?

"Maybe they'll have *The Pilgrim's Progress,*" she suggested quickly. "Grandmother would like that. You could come to see it and stay at our house."

Nearly everybody laughed, but Mother kept looking at the new building as if she were interested, and Willa guessed she was thinking about some of her pretty dresses that she hadn't been able to wear since she left Virginia.

The huge wagon full of boxes and trunks and people had been gathering attention as it rolled slowly through the thick, powdery dust of the street. Men and women stopped to watch, and children followed along behind the wheels.

"Howdy, Mr. Cather," a man called from the wooden sidewalk. "Glad to see you've come to town."

"Thank you, Judge," Father answered, tipping his hat. Mother's back straightened even more while she smiled graciously.

"There's Miner's Store," Willa whispered loudly just as Mr. Miner came out of his new brick building.

"Welcome to Red Cloud, Charles," he called, and then he bowed to Willa's mother who nodded her head in return and lightly tipped her parasol. Willa decided at once that, except for her father, Mr. Miner was the most distinguished-looking man she knew, with his curly black hair, well-brushed mustache, and natty clothes.

But she didn't have time to look at him any longer, for Grandfather was urging the horses around the corner and she wanted to hear what Father was saying to Mother.

"Now Virginia," she heard, "I hope you aren't expecting too much. I tried for six months, you know, and this is the only place I could find to rent. But it's close to the stores and good neighbors. Maybe later, if the mortgage and loan business does well, we can—"

Without warning, the wagon swung again to the south, only a block from Webster Street, and then drew to a halt. Willa read the sign on the corner, "Third and Cedar," while the boys pushed against her and shouted to be let out.

"That?!" Mother exclaimed. "But—but how can we invite anyone into such a little place?"

Father frowned. "I told you it was small, but you wanted to come."

"Now Virginia," Grandma Boak said soothingly, "we'll do just fine. Maybe it's bigger than it looks."

"*Ten* people in that little place," was all Mother could say. "It probably has only one bedroom."

"Two," Father muttered as he jumped down to assist the women.

Willa and Bess stood on the walk and looked at the narrow little white frame house set in a dry, scraggly yard. It backed up to its nearest neighbor like a forlorn stray dog, as though it had got there by mistake and then decided to stay.

The boys dashed around to the rear, but the rest of the family trooped in wearily. There was no mistake. It *was* too small, with little cut-up rooms—one leading into another so that there would be no privacy for anyone. Odd pieces of worn furniture stood around the base-burner in the sitting room.

Slowly they pushed on through the two tiny high-ceilinged bedrooms on the north side, one behind the other. The narrow dining room was along the south side with a small piece of a room between it and the kitchen. That was all.

Willa wandered out by the fuel shed and tried the squeaky handle of the old pump. For a minute she had a vision of the huge house in Virginia, but she didn't want that either. Nebraska was better—lots better. Only where could she ever play or do anything without being told to hush?

The boys were in the kitchen now, begging for food, while Grandma Boak and Margie leaned over the stove. Willa slipped back in. There was a door from the kitchen that she hadn't investigated.

Carefully, so that no one would notice, she opened it and crept silently up the dusty steps. Round a corner she crept and then up more steps until a bright shaft of west sun struck her.

"Oh!" she cried, amazed. "Roscoe! Douglas! Come look!" She stamped her feet to attract attention. Before her was the biggest space she had seen in any home in Nebraska. It ran all the way from the back to the very front of the house.

"It's *huge*," she cried as the boys and Margie came scrambling up. "Why it's as big as Doubting Castle that Grandmother read about in *The Pilgrim's Progress*."

Roscoe held his nose. "Phew!" he said. "Looks more like the dungeon with all those cobwebs." He raced down the length of the attic, knocking great webs from the bare rafters and jumping over the old mattresses and bedsprings. "It's a dungeon, Douglas," he shouted to his brother.

"The Dungeon of the Giant Despair!" Willa cried, picking up an old bed slat and racing down and back. "We'll have a play! I'll be the Giant. You're Christian and Douglas is Hopeful. And—and Margie—" She looked at poor Margie cowering by the steps. "Come on, Margie. You'll have to be the Giant's wife. We have to get rid of these—these trespassers. Come on!"

Back and forth they raced, leaping over beds and striking the rafters with their sticks until the air was thick with dust. Margie still cowered by the stairs looking nothing at all like the Giant's wife.

"You stop now," she began to sob. "You stop or I'll call your ma. She won't like all that dirt all over things. You stop now," she howled, rushing down the stairs.

And so the play ended.

"Aren't you ashamed, Willie," Grandma Boak said reproachfully from the top of the steps while they listened to Margie sobbing below. "Now you march right down and tell her you're sorry, and then you three get the broom and some rags and set this place to rights. We'll need it tonight, if we're all going to sleep."

Willa worked harder than she had ever worked before. With the help of the boys, young as they were, she pulled down the cobwebs from the rough rafters, swept the floor, and at last set up the beds side by side under the eaves.

Finally Mother came up to inspect. "Yes," she said as if she were answering a question in her own mind, "the boys can sleep here. That will take care of two of us."

"The boys!" Willa gasped. "I'm going to sleep here too. It's mine. It's my very own. I *found* it."

"But Willa! An attic! Bess wouldn't want to sleep up here."

"Then she needn't. We cleaned it up. It's ours! If I can't sleep here I won't stay. I'll go back to the farm with Grandfather!" She threw herself face down on a mattress, her arms outstretched, and clung to it as though it might be torn from her.

Mother stared at her for a moment. Then abruptly

· 63 ·

she shrugged her shoulders and turned back. "Oh, it doesn't matter, I suppose—for a while at least. That leaves only seven of us to find room for."

Much later, after a cold supper, everybody was settled at last—Mother and Father in one bedroom, Bess and the two youngest children in the other. Grandma stretched her tired frame on a narrow cot in the little area off the dining room, and Margie found a place in the loft over the kitchen.

While the boys slept, Willa lay for a long time looking at the stars through a small window. Around her moved the princes and queens and giants of all the stories and plays that she had read or heard. No matter what anyone said, it was not an attic. It was a great hall, and she had been the one to discover it!

CHAPTER SEVEN

IT TOOK little time to explore the house on Cedar Street,
once the attic had been discovered and claimed. But Red
Cloud was new territory, and Willa went over it, inch
by inch. Up one street and down the other she roamed,
sometimes pulling Douglas or Jessie on a small red
wagon, but more often alone. Not content with only
the fronts of the buildings, she explored the alleys, too.

Everyone at home was so busy getting settled that
she was seldom missed, but one day her mother met her
at the door as she ambled contentedly up the front walk.
Willa had tied her hair back from her face with an old

piece of rope that she had picked up behind Miner's Store when she was trying to read the names on some of the dry-goods boxes: interesting names like St. Louis and San Francisco. Her curls, which her mother had insisted upon brushing that morning, kept dropping over her eyes when she leaned down. And so she had tied them back.

There were long black smudges on her arms and face, too, from the sooty fence she had climbed, down by the depot. One forlorn spotted calf in a stock pen was trying to nibble the few dry weeds in a corner. Willa picked all the grass she could carry in one arm, climbed the fence, and dropped it over. The calf looked up at her with big, brown, grateful eyes.

"I'll come to see you tomorrow," she promised when she left him.

It had been a lovely afternoon. But now Mother's eyes flashed.

"Where have you been, Willa?" she asked, exasperated.

"Oh, to the nicest places. There was a poor little calf—"

"A calf! I thought you wanted to come to town to see *people,* not *animals.* Well, Mrs. Miner came to call with two of her daughters—about your age. And I didn't even know where you were!"

Willa could see how disappointed her mother was— her first real call in her own home in Nebraska, and things hadn't been just as she wanted them. Suddenly she felt very sorry for her pretty mother who loved good times and had had so few this past year.

"They want you to come over tomorrow to play. They live in the big square house in the next block— you can see it from your bedroom." She never used the word "attic" any more.

"Oh, good! Were they nice?"

Mother's face softened and she smiled dreamily, remembering. "Lovely," she said. "Just lovely. They brought a sunshine cake for our supper and I served them coffee and some of Grandma's cookies. I think, from something she said, that Mrs. Miner is a *musician*." The way she said it made a musician a very special person.

The next morning, her curls brushed and her blue checked gingham dress clean and starched, Willa waved good-by to Mother and then walked sedately around the corner and started down Third Street. But as soon as she heard the door close she glanced quickly back to check and then slipped around to the old shed at the rear of the lot. A family of kittens lived there, and Father had been talking about giving them away.

"Here, kitty, kitty, kitty—" she called softly, and

three little gray balls of fur came tumbling toward her. Quickly she picked up one of them and hurried back to the street. *Any* girl would want a kitten, but her mother might not think so.

At the Miners' gate she set the kitten down gently, pulled a pink ribbon from her pocket, and knelt down to tie it around the soft little neck. She was intent upon getting the bow right when she slowly became aware of sounds coming from the house. Someone was playing a piano. She had heard music before—folk songs and hymns, of course—but never anything like this. There was a wonderful rhythm to it that made Willa want to swing round and round, and yet there was more—much more. It was full and rich and—

Without knowing where her feet led her she moved toward the rush of sound—through the gate—up the walk—across the porch—until she stood with her forehead pressed against the screen door.

In the room beyond, someone sat at the piano, a plump little woman with a soft knot of light hair piled on top of her head. Willa's eyes were drawn at once to her hands—soft, flexible white hands that flew over the keys to send thrills up and down her back.

How long she stood there she did not know, but she must have been squeezing the kitten under her arm, for all at once it began to meow and claw at the screen.

The music stopped in the middle of a phrase and a warm, jolly voice said, "Oh, there you are! We've been expecting you. And you've brought your kitten!"

The screen door opened against her and one of the hands that had been performing the miracle of music took her by the arm and led her inside. Still she was speechless as she stood before that piano in wonder.

"Wh—what was that you were playing?" she asked at last.

"Oh, did you like it? It was a Chopin waltz—one of my favorites," Mrs. Miner answered with a gay bounce to her voice that made Willa turn to look up into her face.

"Can anybody play that? I mean—anybody like me?" Willa spread out one square brown hand that had held a pony's reins, pulled her over fences, dug into the Nebraska earth in search of plants. It was scarred from recent cuts, not at all flexible, and gray with dust from the kitten's fur.

"Well, not everybody," Mrs. Miner answered truthfully. "But anyone can try. Mary is taking lessons now. She does quite well.

"Mary," she called up the stairs. "Willa is here. Hurry! She's brought her kitten."

"Everybody calls me Willie. I like it better," Willa explained as Mary came bounding down the steps. "I brought this for you," she added, thrusting the kitten into Mary's arms before she had a chance to say hello.

That was the beginning for Willa and Mary Miner. They were fast friends at once. On good days they swung from the apple trees; romped with the kittens; or rode out on Mary's pony, Billy, to explore farther than Willa's feet could take her—beyond the depot and down along the shallow, sandy Republican River. On rainy days they had circuses in the Miners' barn or plays in the Cathers' big attic bedroom, which Mary agreed was like a feudal hall.

But many of the best hours for Willa were spent at the Miners' when all the children gathered around the piano to listen to Mrs. Miner play. On special days she would play parts of operas she had heard when she lived in Norway. She told the stories as she went along, describing the gorgeous costumes and singing bits of the arias. Then the cries of the Valkyrie maidens, as they rode to battles, seemed to echo through the air. Willa could hear them even after she snuggled down on a cold night in her attic bed—her feet pressed against a hot brick that she had carried up from the kitchen. There was so much more in the world than she had ever dreamed of! What else was she missing?

But on Tuesday afternoons Willa was excluded from

the Miner house altogether. That was when Professor Shindelmeisser came to give Mary her lesson. The other Miner children were sent out of the house, Mrs. Miner took her place on the settee and folded her hands on her short lap, and the lesson began.

Willa sulked around her own house on the first Tuesdays after she saw the little old man, with the funny black hat set squarely on his head and the music case under his arm, trot up the Miners' front walk. Why couldn't *she* listen, too? But after several Tuesdays she began to make plans. If she slipped into the Miners' barn before the professor arrived, she might be able to get through the kitchen while Mrs. Miner was opening the front door. Then she could hide in the hall closet close to the sitting room, and no one would know!

One rainy day, after she had said good-by to Mary and Mrs. Miner and started dutifully for home, she slipped back into the barn and watched.

"There he is," she breathed at last. The back door stood open—everything was ready.

"One—two—three—" she counted slowly, to make the seconds fly. She mustn't try too soon—or too late. "Four—five—six—" The professor must be on the porch! "Seven—eight—nine—"

Crouching low, she dashed, shoes in hand, through

the door and into the kitchen. No one was around. A plate of cookies stood on the table, waiting for the teacher.

"Come in, come in, Professor Shindelmeisser," she heard. "My, my, what a day. Let me take your hat."

She had just enough time to slip into the closet and leave the door ajar.

"Ya. Ya. It iss so," she heard.

Why he's from Germany like the Lambrechts! Willa thought when she heard him speak. Henry played the harmonica. Maybe all Germans played music!

There was more talk about the weather and the height of the piano stool and then, when the clock finished striking, the lesson began.

"Da scales first," Willa heard.

Mary worked up and down, up and down the keyboard. "No, no. *Dis* finger—so." Then Mary played the pieces that Willa had heard over and over. Now and then the little man would rap hard on something and utter a few words. Mary would go over a passage until he was satisfied.

Willa almost fell asleep in the stuffy closet. It wasn't very exciting after all—just more practice. But it *could* be. Somehow she knew, from the way Mrs. Miner acted, that this little man was different. He had lived around musicians, she was sure. He had been to operas and concerts in big, fascinating cities that she was only beginning to dream of. What stories he could tell! But how would she ever hear them unless she could take lessons too? And the Cathers had no piano.

Her thoughts bubbled on while the lesson continued. If only she had a piano, maybe she could have lessons. That was it! A piano!

In the middle of one of Mary's noisier pieces Willa slipped cautiously out the back door, through the barn, around several blocks, and then back to Cedar Street and home. She knew that if her mother approved she would have no difficulty with her gentle father. But Mother had very definite ideas about things.

Slowly and sadly she wandered into the kitchen. Mother was rocking the baby and talking happily with Grandma and Margie about the Christmas program and supper that the women of the church were planning at yesterday's meeting. She was already accepted in all their activities and now they were looking to her for ideas.

The smell of hot gingerbread almost brought a happy smile to Willa's face, too, but carefully she kept her downcast expression.

"Why, Willie, what ails you, child?" Grandma exclaimed. "Are you sick?"

"No," she answered as she slumped into a chair.

"Then what *is* the matter?" Mother asked. "Did you quarrel with Mary? Is that it?"

"Oh, no. Mary is my *very* best friend. Only she's having her piano lesson. It must be wonderful to play all that lovely music."

"Why, Willa," her mother exclaimed. "I didn't know you cared a fig for music."

"But I do! Mrs. Miner plays such wonderful music for us. And Mary does, too. Mary plays for Sunday school and she's just a year older," she added significantly.

Mrs. Cather sat thinking for a few minutes, little lines deepening between her eyes. At last she spoke while Willa held her breath. "I believe I'll talk to Mrs. Miner," she said.

"Oh, Mother!" Willa cried.

She threw her arms around her mother and then dashed upstairs. It was all settled. She could tell. The Cathers would get a piano and she would have lessons from that interesting little man.

The next day, Mother called on Mrs. Miner and that evening she and Father had a long, private conference. One day a piano was moved into the sitting room and placed against the wall. It was not a beautiful piano. Several of the keys were chipped and the tone was harsh, but Willa could scarcely eat her supper, she was so excited.

The next week, on Tuesday, Professor Shindelmeisser came up *her* walk before he went to the Miners'. Slices of spice cake were ready. Her lessons began!

At first Willa tried mightily.

"Da scales," the little professor would say. "First da scales. You cannot play pieces widout da fingers move right."

And so Willa thumped up and down the keys at his bidding. Sometimes one finger, sometimes another, crossed at the proper time.

"No, no! Da middle finger—so!" he would exclaim and mop his brow. "And please—lightly, not like da hammers." He would cover his ears.

"You show me," Willa liked to say. "It sounds so nice."

Whenever she could get him to play a little for her she had won a victory. The theme of a concerto was enough to start the questions going. "What is that?" "Did you really hear it with a whole orchestra?" "How many musicians?" "In Prague? Is it a beautiful city? Tell me about it." Eagerly she would listen, careful to watch his lips for a sign of hesitation so that she could be ready with a new question.

Finally exhausted, the poor little professor would shake out a huge, sodden handkerchief and run it around his moist, rumpled collar. Sometimes he would pull himself up to his full height. "Miss Villie," he would say. "Da lesson. Da scales. No more talk!"

Other times he would drop pathetically onto a chair, wring his hands, and try to appeal to her. "Miss Villie, please do da lesson. Your mama iss listening."

Then Willa felt ashamed. The shabby little man needed to earn his fee.

But scales and exercises were so dull. Yet how could she ever forget the stories he told of the crown prince and his glittering company of bejeweled women and handsome men seated in the royal box of a great opera house? Especially there was the thrilling time when the prince leaned forward and tossed a rose onto the stage to the beautiful prima donna, while all in the great theater stood to applaud and shout their praise.

She and Mary had acted that scene for days in one end of the attic room with a packing box for a stage. Christmas tree ornaments were their gorgeous jewels and medals. Would the new opera house ever be finished?

But through it all, Willa made almost no progress at the piano. Each Tuesday Professor Shindelmeisser left, damp and dejected, for the Miners'. "Dat Villie Cadder," he would moan to Mrs. Miner. "Vat vill I do?"

Finally, one Tuesday, he stalked out of the house just as Mrs. Cather came up the walk.

"Madam," he said as he swept his worn black hat from his head, "I must speak vid you."

"Why, of course, Professor," she answered brightly. The odd little man always looked so worried, but Mrs. Miner had assured her—

"*Now,* Madam. And Miss Villie also."

Willa's mother looked at his agitated face. There was really something wrong. Perhaps he was ill. She turned and led the way into the house, wondering what to say to console him.

When Willa saw their expressions, she knew she was in trouble. What if the lessons should stop—and just when she was about to find out how that exciting Wagnerian opera ended? Will Brünnhilde live or die? What will happen to the cursed ring of the Rhine Maidens?

In the front room they sat down solemnly, the professor perched on the edge of his chair.

"Madam," he said again, "I regret to tell you—Miss Villie iss not learning. All da time it iss talk, talk, talk— qvestions, qvestions, qvestions— You are wasting your money, Madam." He folded his hands in his lap and lowered his eyes, waiting.

Mrs. Cather rapped her fingers angrily on the arm

of her chair. "Is this true, Willa?" she asked sharply.

"Oh, no! I'm *not* wasting my time," Willa cried. "I've learned and learned—all about the orchestras and the wonderful operas and—and the beautiful cities—and the people." Her breath caught in her throat.

There was a long silence while she was afraid even to breathe. At last her mother stood up and smiled cheerfully at the little music teacher.

"I must see to the baby," she said, moving toward the door, her mind already elsewhere. "It's quite all right, Professor Shindelmeisser. Willa seems to be learning a great deal. There is little enough in Red Cloud for her. Just give her what she wants." And she walked lightly back toward the kitchen.

Fine snow was beginning to fall as Willa stood at the window watching the professor move down the walk and around the corner. His hat was still in his hand and his shabby overcoat hung away from his neck as though he had started to put it on but had forgotten to finish.

Willa couldn't help giggling when he almost bumped into their next-door neighbor, Mrs. Weiner, without even knowing she had opened her gate. He just kept on shaking his head and talking to himself as he shuffled along. But Willa could easily imagine what he was saying: "Dat Villie Cadder! Vat she do next?"

CHAPTER EIGHT

WINTER passed quickly in Red Cloud. Even before the arrival of the first northbound birds, the ice broke on the Republican River and began to move downstream. On this bright Saturday morning people stood in groups on the streets of the town, a mile from the river, to listen for the great thunderous booms and talk about other years. Three years ago the ice had "gone out" late. Last year it had been early. But whenever the time came, everyone knew that spring would not be far away.

Willa rode south behind Mary on the Miners' pony, Billy, thinking of Boots and the Lambrechts and especially of Annie Sadilek, whose frail little father had died during the winter. Soon now, she could go out to visit at the farm and ride the trails again to see all her old friends.

But today she and Mary were headed for the river along with most of the other children of the town, some men, and a few women. It was still a wintry day, but somehow it didn't *seem* cold, with spring so near. There was a throb in the air, as though a giant pulse were slowly beginning to beat again.

"Sounds like the Fourth of July," one big boy yelled to another as he raced by them. Willa touched Billy's flank with her heel and the pony bounded ahead.

"Think you're smart," the other boy shouted as they galloped past, but nobody cared.

"Stay back!" a man cried out as they drew up at the bank. "Mary Miner, you get that pony back. You know this river acts up."

Willa peered toward the opposite shore. Only last week the river seemed a solid sheet of ice. But today it was slipping downstream. She could see open patches of angry water. Along the bank, here and there, huge chunks of ice had piled up on each other to dig into the mud and sand.

Then suddenly, as if the added weight were more than it could bear, the ground shuddered beneath them and Billy neighed and reared, tossing his head in fear. There was a noise like a great sigh, and the earth directly in front of them gave up its struggle and slipped into the turbulent water.

"Back! Everybody back!" men shouted while the crowd scurried to safer ground. But Willa slid from the dancing pony to watch the great chunk of earth swirl round and round, dipping its willows and scrub ash crazily from side to side. Soon it was in midstream and then a pile of ice shoved it high onto a small sandy island.

"Mary!" Willa cried as her friend pulled her to safer ground. "Look! That's our island! See what's happened to it. It's changed!" It was the island they had waded to one day in the fall.

"Oh, the island never stays the same," Mary explained as though she supposed Willa knew. "It's different every year. Sometimes it's big and sometimes it's small. One year it wasn't there at all—just like magic."

"Just like magic," Willa sighed. "An enchanted island! Oh, Mary, just as soon as we can, let's really explore it. There are probably robbers' dens and buried treasures. Maybe we can find some secret places where no one has ever been before!"

Mary looked at Willa and then back at the island again. Could all that be on a stretch of sand and scrub trees in the Republican River? Somehow Willa made it seem so.

"Not even Coronado?" Mary asked.

"Who's Coronado?"

"Oh, I've heard people talk about him," Mary answered airily, glad for once to know something that Willa had never heard of. "He was a famous Spanish explorer."

"Spanish!" Willa had never seen a Spaniard. "What did he do?"

"Well—I—I—Willie, let's go home. I'm *cold* and everybody's leaving." She swung up onto the pony's back before Willa could start asking questions that she couldn't answer.

"But we've just *come*. I want to see what happens to our island. What about that Spaniard?"

"Well—well the men at the store talk a lot about him. My father knows, too."

Reluctantly Willa took her place behind Mary just as the ice split again with a mighty *BOOM!* that echoed up and down the river. Mary had seen this before, but *she* never had. Yet if they got back before Mr. Miner left for his dinner, she might hear about this Coronado. What was a Spaniard exploring in Red Cloud?

Back in the store, a group of old men sat around the

stove as they did nearly every day in winter. In spring they moved their chairs out to the sidewalk, where they could prop them back against the brick wall. But in spite of the excitement on the river, this was another day to sit around the fire with friends and keep the chill out of the bones a little longer.

Willa and Mary slipped in quietly and tiptoed up the back steps to fill their pockets with hard bright-colored candies from a huge candy barrel.

"Shh," Mary cautioned when Willa tried to tilt the barrel to get some of her favorite kind—red outside, then white, with a tiny red rose in the center. They tasted more like raspberries than roses, but she liked to hold one in her cheek until everything except the flower had disappeared.

Quietly they tiptoed down again, careful to miss the step that squeaked.

The men were still talking about the ice. "Worst time was in '75," one old-timer insisted, skillfully squirting a stream of tobacco juice into the open door of the stove. "Came sudden like, and ripped off six acres of good wheat land from my place. Some feller on the Kansas side got my six acres. Shoulda made him pay me fer 'em."

A slow chuckle passed around the circle. As it subsided, Willa was ready.

"Maybe Coronado got them, do you think?"

Chairs that had been tilted on their back two legs thumped to all four. The chuckle grew into a hearty laugh, and Mr. Miner, behind the counter, joined in.

"Why, Willie Cather," he joked, "I thought you'd discovered everything about Red Cloud, including my candy barrel. Coronado didn't want a few acres of anybody's land. He could have had the whole country if he got up this far a couple of hundred years ago. He was looking for the Seven Cities of Gold."

"Seven cities of gold! In Nebraska?"

"Sure thing," the same old-timer chimed in when Mary's father turned to wait on a customer. "Him and his soldiers came all the way from Mexico, dressed fancy, too, with armor and spears and the like. Hunted all over the West. Folks tell they found big canyons and mighty fast rivers—whale of a lot faster than ours—but nary a city of gold."

The other old men nodded in agreement.

"No gold? Are you sure?"

"Folks say so. Course you never know—"

Willa's head whirled. All this right here in Red Cloud! First the enchanted island and now Coronado in shining armor. It was almost too much for one day.

"Now, Sam," Mr. Miner said, back in time to hear

the last remarks, "nobody knows *for sure* that he got this far. You better not tell too many stories to Willie Cather or she'll be out digging up the whole riverbank looking for treasures."

But Willa didn't even listen to their laughter. Already, in her mind, she was opening a rusty chest to find it heaped with pieces of eight—just like Jim Hawkins in that new book *Treasure Island* that a salesman gave to Mrs. Miner. Willa had read it twice already.

It was some time, however, before the Miner and Cather children could get to the island. But luckily, the swift spring current left a submerged bar of sand between one end of the island and a point on the shore. Willa came down often to watch it and test the swiftness of the water.

Finally, on a sunny spring morning, she led the way. She wore a pair of old trousers rolled above her knees and carried a long stick in her hand. Behind her were Mary and Margie Miner, and Roscoe and Douglas.

"Mary, you hold onto my belt, and the rest of you make a chain. And *don't let go*," Willa commanded. Cautiously she poked the stick into the sand before her until she found sure footing. Then she moved ahead. The frigid water swirled around their ankles.

"Hurry up, Willie," Douglas cried.

"It's not cold, Douglas," Margie Miner boasted through her chattering teeth. She was the tomboy of the Miner family.

"We'll get warm in no time," Willa called back. "Look at all that dry wood piled up by the ice. We'll build a fire and run around."

"How you going to build a fire?"

"You'll see." There was no use explaining that she had been planning this trip ever since the ice broke. If it failed—if anyone fell into the river— She hadn't meant to bring Douglas, who was only six, but he had begged to come.

"Hold on tight, Douglas," she called as one foot oozed into a soft spot. "I'll take you piggy-back when we go home."

At last they came out of the water onto a stretch of warm sand.

"Look!" Roscoe cried as he scooped the fine warm grains over his feet and up onto his ankles. "It's like an oven—like warm bricks in bed. We don't need a fire."

"See? I told you," Willa boasted. "It's summer, almost, and this is our very own island." She thrust her stick into the sand and struck a pose. "I, Willie Cather, now claim this island for the United States government."

"Oh, no!" Mary protested. "For the Miner and Cather families!"

"But—if Coronado claimed it for the Spanish government—"

"Well then," Mary persisted, "for the Miners and Cathers, who are citizens of Nebraska and the United States of America."

"And the world!" Roscoe whooped. "Let's see what we've got!"

They raced off, forgetting about their cold feet. Up over washed-out cottonwood roots they scrambled, and down by sandy pools where tadpoles fluttered through the shallow water as they approached. They lingered for a long time in the grove of cottonwoods where purple violets spread a thick royal carpet for the adventurers just as they may have for Coronado two hundred years before, Willa thought. Then back they romped, past a huge rock in the very center of the island. At last, exhausted, they threw themselves down on the sand again.

"Look," Willa said as she drew a package from inside her jacket. "Sandwiches. Here's one for you Mary—and Margie—and Roscoe—and—and—"

"Douglas!" Roscoe screamed. "Where's Douglas?"

There was no answer.

"Douglas!" they all called at once, but only the birds answered, chattering and fluttering their wings in protest.

Willa sprang to her feet and looked around at the white, frightened faces. "Mary, you go to the far end," she commanded. "Roscoe, hunt in the grove. Margie, you—you look all round that pile of roots. Maybe he fell." Her lips started to quiver but she turned away quickly. "I'll search the center of the island. Hurry! And shout if you find him."

Soon, from every corner of the island, plaintive calls of "Douglas!" "Douglas!" came back to Willa. But there was no answer—no triumphant shout from one of the searchers. Willa prodded with a stick into every bush and clump around the big rock. The sun was hot overhead now, and her arms burned from scratches. But her brother was not near the rock.

She tried to remember, but her pounding heart seemed to drown her thoughts. He had fallen behind to pick violets in the grove, but she had taken his hand then and helped him over a log. And he had wanted to watch the tadpoles— The tadpoles! Suddenly Willa remembered that they had passed near the pool again on their way back to the sandy beach.

She raced to the spot. "Douglas," she called softly. *"Please,* Douglas. Answer me."

At last a soft reproachful whisper came from under a bush by a shallow pool. "Sh! Aw, Willie, you scared 'em again. What you making all that noise for? I almost had one by the tail, but you scared him away."

"Oh, Douglas!" Willa cried, throwing her arms around her brother until he pushed her away in protest. "I found him! I found him!" she screamed, while joyous shouts answered her from every side.

When they all assembled again, exhausted and hungrier than before, and set to work brushing the sand from the lunch, Willa began to worry. If her mother or Mrs. Miner learned about this—

"Raise your right hands," she said suddenly.

"Oh, Willie, we're hungry!" Margie protested.

"Do it anyway. Everybody!" She looked so fierce that no one dared object. Everyone's right hand went up as she had commanded.

"Now swear that this will be our secret island. *No* one is to know except us—about Douglas getting lost and everything. Or maybe we won't ever be allowed to come again."

"I swear," they all said at once and began devouring their sandy lunch.

Only Douglas protested. "Aw, Willie, I wasn't lost. You just scared my tadpoles," he said.

CHAPTER NINE

As THE blistering heat descended upon Nebraska to ripen the corn and turn the long grass red again, the river drew Willa and the other explorers more and more often. Who would want to play in a stifling attic room when there was a cool river to wade and a magic island to roam? Even the Miners' barn lost its appeal when prickly straw stuck to their moist skin and tickled their noses.

Along the river someone could always find an Indian arrowhead in the clay banks or a lazy turtle dozing among the cattails and reeds. Or they would wade to the island and go on with their endless search for Coronado's treasure.

They were sure it was there, especially after Willa uncovered a rusty can filled with odd nails and pieces of wire. It had been lost by an early explorer, she declared, and no one doubted her. For the next week they all acted the best scenes from *Treasure Island*—especially the finding of the treasure chest.

Only hunger drove them home.

Then, unless one of the Catherton neighbors had stopped by to visit, Willa usually slipped out again after sundown. The house was so warm and full of people. Cousin Bess and some young man were usually on the front porch. Baby Jim often fretted from colic or the heat until he dropped asleep. And the other children, too tired to stay awake, too restless to sleep, kept running in and out.

Besides, Willa had discovered the delights of summer evenings when she could be near people and yet apart from them. She liked to sit on the edge of the board walk alongside Miner's Store and rub her feet in the powdery dust of the road. The old men were outside now, and sometimes Mr. Miner joined them before closing time.

If Willa kept very still she could hear all sorts of things. She heard about the early days when Red Cloud was only a stockade; about Indian raids; about Captain Garber, who later became governor of Nebraska. There was always a heated argument sometime during the evening about the government in Washington, D.C.

But the best time came after the stores began to close and the lights in houses went out, one by one. For then she could go down alone to watch the late train come through. Unless someone got off or on, it did not stop. But there was mystery behind the darkened windows and the occasional flashes of light that sent her thoughts racing far away from Red Cloud.

And while she waited, counting the white tails of jack rabbits as they scurried through the dry weeds, she could sometimes hear exciting music. It came from the little box-houses of Mexican workers across the tracks. Sometimes it was just a lonely voice sobbing a sad melody. Or maybe someone strummed a guitar faster and faster while voices rose in strange, wild song.

Her father had told her that these people came all the way up from Mexico to work on the railroad. They must have seen the same country that Coronado saw! As the train whistled and flashed past the station, Willa vowed each time that someday she too would take that road to the Southwest to see the magic land of brave explorers in shining armor.

But one cool fall day everything else faded into the past when great news flashed through the town. Mary Miner bounded into the Cather kitchen while Margie Anderson and Grandma Boak were dishing up the mush and fried ham.

"Where's Willie?" she cried. "Tell her to hurry! They've come!"

"Shh!" Grandma cautioned. "You'll wake the baby. What's come?"

"The *seats!* The seats for the opera house, that's what. Papa's taking the delivery cart down to the depot to help. Everybody's going!"

She raced toward the stairs before Margie could stop her, nearly knocking down Willa as she came in, still in her long nightgown, her clothes in her hand.

"The seats are here?" Willa cried, pulling on her clothes and gulping down great spoonfuls of mush while Grandma protested. "They've *really* come?"

It was almost too much to believe at last, for there had been so many delays. She folded a slice of ham between two squares of corn bread and dashed through the door after Mary, while Roscoe and Douglas cried "Wait! Wait!" behind her.

Men from all over town turned out to load and unload the seats and help bolt them in rows across the floor of the theater. They shouted to each other over the pounding and scraping. Finally they barred all the children from the noisy room so that they could get on with the work.

But Willa knew another entrance. She and Mary sped around to the rear, slipped through a small alley window, and crept silently up the dusky back steps.

Imagine having *two* curtains on one stage! They hid in the folds of the red velvetlike ones and ran their fingers along the silky fringe. They felt the crank that would raise the drop curtain.

But after a while Willa could stand this quiet no longer. Everyone else was *doing* something. She tiptoed cautiously halfway across the stage behind the drop curtain.

"Come on. I'm Macbeth and you're Lady Macbeth," she hissed to Mary as she struck a pose. She threw back her head and gazed mournfully into space.

"My dearest love, Duncan comes here tonight," she quoted.

This was a scene they had acted before. Mary knew what to do. She wrung her hands and implored, "And when goes hence?"

"Tomorrow, as he purposes."

"O, never shall sun that morrow see!" Mary declared. "Your face, my Thane—"

"Mary! Is that you?" a stern voice demanded. It was Mr. Miner.

Willa and Mary stood paralyzed as the walls of the Scottish castle melted around them. Then someone rolled up the curtain.

"Willie Cather, too. I should have known!"

Mr. Miner stood in front of the stage, his arms folded in disapproval. Behind him all work stopped while everyone stared.

"Oh, never are we agoin' to see the sun, my love," a high voice mocked as the two actresses fled, red-faced, down the stairs.

There were speeches and programs later that month. But not until the new red brick had been baptized with snow did anything more exciting happen on that stage. Then one day, as the children wandered home from school, taking turns at pulling each other on their sleds, a boy in front let out a whoop.

"Posting bills!" he shouted and everyone began to run. Willa ran too.

Ahead was a stranger. He looked something like the salesmen who came into town on the Burlington and Missouri trains to show their lines of goods in the sample rooms at the Holland House hotel. Yet he was different, Willa decided as she came closer. He walked with a jauntier air, as though he felt very important. And he carried a handful of papers. Now and then he would stop to nail one to a fence or a building and then move on.

"Look out there, kids," he warned when they caught up with him.

Willa craned her neck to read the print. "What is it?" she cried, pinching Mary's arm. Mary always knew about things, since she had lived in Red Cloud longer.

"Playbills! The players are coming! Oh, they're going to play *Uncle Tom's Cabin*. See—it says next Saturday night."

Playbills. *Uncle Tom's Cabin*. Willa stared at the sheet of yellow paper, lost in the words she read there. Great blobs of snow splashed on it, but she brushed them away as soon as they fell. The other children followed the stranger down the street. She was alone in the world of her imagination.

"The manager has much pleasure in announcing—" she whispered as the scenes of the story she knew so well spun in her head. Slowly she ran a cold finger down the long list of characters: Uncle Tom, Eliza, Little Eva, Mr. St. Claire, Topsy, Simon Legree—she knew them all. And on Saturday night they would be in the Red Cloud Opera House!

All week the Cather home was in turmoil. The entire family was going to the play and all the best clothes had to be pressed and lengthened and mended. Mother kept changing her mind about what she would wear, but she smiled and hummed a tune while her needle flew.

Margie worried and mumbled from morning to night. "You'll get all them fine clothes dirty," she kept saying over and over. Mr. Cather had to explain to her every evening that this would not be like one of Willa's plays. But the next morning she worried again. She flatly refused to accompany them, even though Willa promised to hold her hand until the play ended.

At noon on Saturday, an impatient crowd around the depot trampled the snow to gray slush. Willa blew on her hands and jumped up and down close to the soot-covered cars as the train pulled in, trying to see through each steamy window. At last the wheels screeched to a halt and the conductor threw open the door of the parlor car.

Willa held her breath as the company of players hustled out, one by one. Her eyes followed every gesture. The men in their bowler hats and long overcoats strode briskly to the baggage car and then paced up and down while they checked each trunk and suitcase. She caught a glimpse of a flashing stickpin and a glittering ring on a hand that held a fat cigar.

Then the women descended. Some looked bored and sleepy; others waved to the crowd. At last the leading lady appeared in the doorway, smiling and shaking her yellow curls. She was wrapped in a long fur coat and cuddled something under her arm. The whole crowd gasped. It was a tiny dog dressed in its own little blanket!

She waved gaily and blew kisses while everyone shouted in delight. Then she threw a flimsy scarf over her face and swept across the platform to the waiting carriage.

That evening after Willa had dressed and Mother had brushed her curls for the second time, she stood in front of the little cracked mirror in Grandma's room and tried to smile and shake her curls in the gay, assured manner of the leading lady. But it was no use. She would just have to go on playing the boys' parts in the plays. She could never look languid or delicate enough for Little Eva.

Afterward, Willa tried to recall the evening from beginning to end, but it was all a jumble of what she saw and how she felt until she didn't know what was real and what was imagined. Even the audience looked unreal—the men in their best black broadcloth coats and jeweled stickpins, the women decked out in every piece of finery they could gather. And there was Mrs. Holland who ran the hotel where the players stayed; she was flushed with her importance and actually wearing, at last, the dazzling diamond necklace and earrings that people whispered about but had never seen. This *couldn't* be Red Cloud!

An orchestra played a lively Negro tune and then the lights went out, the footlights came up, and the curtains parted. There stood Uncle Tom himself, picking cotton from a real-looking bush while he hummed a mournful melody.

From there on, Willa lived with the characters. Her heart leaped with fright at the sound of the barking hounds and howling wind behind stage when Eliza, clutching her baby, dashed across the ice. She moaned over the tragic parting of Uncle Tom from his family when he was sold down the river. Tears soaked the front of her dress when angelic Little Eva gave her dying gasps. And her sodden handkerchief was twisted into a hard rope by the time Uncle Tom breathed his last.

That night Willa lay awake in her bed with a warm brick at her feet while fine snow sifted down through the shingles and sprinkled her face. How could the others laugh and joke after the play was over, just as though it hadn't happened? Maybe when she got older she could too, but deep inside her she knew that something went on in her imagination that was different— that went deeper—that would be with her forever.

CHAPTER TEN

THE Red Cloud Opera House soon became the center for all kinds of entertainment. Sometimes stock companies stayed for a week and put on a different play every night. There were comic minstrel shows, magicians, and groups of musicians like the wandering Italian minstrels with their dancing bear.

And between the more professional productions, the local dramatic club met often to rehearse such plays as *Led Astray* or *Leah the Forsaken,* though they were always careful to cut out the parts that might offend some people. Willa was usually called upon to do the rewriting, for it was understood that she had "talent."

But the next fall, Willa turned her mind in a new direction. Though she was not quite thirteen, she was large for her age and everyone knew that she read a great deal and so was "different." After her father had a long talk with Mrs. Goudy, the principal, she was permitted to enroll in the high school.

At last she would have a chance really to learn! It had been wonderful, all year, to slip into the Weiners' house next door, lie on the floor in the quiet study, and read from their large stock of books. Sometimes she listened while Mrs. Weiner read in French and then told her the story. But high school was supposed to mean something else. She would be taught all the knowledge of the world!

On the first day she walked into the building and took her place with her classmates. In high hopes, she copied a list of books that she was to buy. After school she went down to Dr. Cook's pharmacy to purchase her supplies.

As she came out, Roscoe and Douglas met her, dragging Jessie and little Jim on the wagon behind them. Mother was ailing again, and they had been instructed to keep the younger children out of the house.

"Come on, Willie," Douglas begged. "Let's go down to the depot to see the train. Grandma says we can stay out till suppertime."

But Willa drew herself up as she had seen her mother do when an important decision had to be made.

"No," she said with dignity. "You children run along and play. I'm in high school now and I have to study. Mrs. Goudy said we must work hard to succeed."

Determinedly she walked home, hugging her books to her chest. Mother sat in the kitchen with Grandma and Margie. Her face was drawn and discouraged. Willa had seen that look before. It always meant there would be another baby in the family. She loved her brothers and sister, but where, in this tiny house, would they put another crying, demanding baby?

"Willa," her mother said as soon as she came in, "I had a talk with your father last night. Now that you're in high school you must have a room of your own."

Willa gasped. Surely she wouldn't have to move downstairs now, out of her beloved attic room!

"B-but where?" she queried, really frightened. And then she stamped her foot and almost shouted so that no one could see the tears coming into her eyes. "I *won't leave* the attic. I *won't!* I *won't!* I couldn't study or think or anything down here!"

Mrs. Cather rose and put a hand on her daughter's shoulder. Willa knew, under the weight of that hand, that this was one of those rare moments when her mother understood her better than anyone else could.

It was like the day when she had wanted so much to learn from Professor Shindelmeisser.

"Willa," she said wearily, "when a young lady is in high school she is beginning to grow into a woman. She must have privacy. Tomorrow the workmen are coming to board up the north wing of the second floor. They will put a door on it and give you a key. Bess will have the front end of the upstairs. You may both go down to the hardware store tomorrow to select your wallpaper."

Still clutching her purchases to her chest, Willa slowly moved up the steps. She dropped her books onto the floor of the north wing and piled pillows beside them. Then she lay down on her back and looked up at the familiar rafters.

The attic would be all cut up into rooms. The rough rafters of her own part would be closed in. Everything would be changed.

"But I'll have a key," she whispered to herself. "I can shut the door if I want to." Sadly she knew that she was beginning to grow up.

Then suddenly, so that the new thoughts would not spoil the pleasure of her first day in high school, she rolled over and picked up the first book.

"*Algebra,*" she read, and she turned the pages.

Slowly her nose crinkled in distaste. Why, it was like the arithmetic that people were always trying to make her learn. How she hated it! She threw the book aside in disgust.

The literature book looked interesting. She thumbed through it. There was a section by American poets: Longfellow, Holmes, Whittier, Lowell, Poe—all the familiar poems that Grandmother Cather used to read aloud during the long winter on the farm! She knew many of them by heart, but she read "The Raven" again, and "The Deacon's Masterpiece." She glanced through *Macbeth* to see if it was all there, and read Lincoln's Gettysburg Address.

When she closed the book she told herself that she was glad to have all the familiar works for her own. But there was a lump of disappointment in her throat that she kept trying to swallow. Would she have to read the same things over and over all year long?

The book entitled *History* was full of maps and names and dates. She promised herself that she would study them very hard so that she would succeed as Mrs. Goudy wanted her to.

Then she opened the book she had been saving for the last. She had glanced inside it in the store. It was called *Natural Science* and contained some fascinating pictures. Here at last was something she had always wanted to know.

She turned to a drawing of the different parts of a

flower. They had names! "Stamen," she pronounced softly. "Pistil." "Style." "Stigma." The words were easy, but it was hard to tell one from the other just by looking at the picture.

Farther along in the book were drawings of small animals, showing the blood vessels and muscles. There was a frog, and a cat—so this was what they would learn! On Saturday she would go hunting for frogs. In the spring Douglas could bring her tadpoles. And the town was full of stray cats!

She read under the north window until she could no longer see the print. A room of her own would be nice after all, she decided. She could light a lamp and study in bed as late as she liked.

The next day she dreamed through the algebra class, tried to listen politely as the other children painfully took turns reading aloud in the English and history classes. Then at last it was time for natural science.

The teacher was a thin, frightened young man who had been to college for one year but had never taught before. He kept clearing his throat and rustling the pages of the book as he talked. He, too, said they must work hard, and he assigned five pages for them to study.

All week the pupils repeated to him what they memorized from the book. Questions ran through Willa's head until she thought it would burst. Several times she raised her hand, but the teacher ignored her. A small microscope gathered dust on a table in the corner. Two alcohol burners beside it looked as though they had never been used.

The next week, she decided what she must do. She started out early one morning to pick some goldenrod. If the teacher knew about flowers, she was going to find out. If he didn't—well, there was just no use trying to get him to teach her any longer.

Before any of the other pupils had reached the school she slipped inside and up the steps to the bleak science room. The young man sat slumped over a book. As Willa came up behind him she saw what he was studying—the lesson for the day. When she cleared her throat, he looked up with that same frightened expression.

"Sir," she said before he could stop her. "I don't understand about this goldenrod. It's different from the flower in the book. And the blossoms are so small I can't tell—" She laid it before him.

The teacher's face flushed a deep red and his lips trembled in anger.

"Kerchoo!" he sneezed, groping for his handkerchief. "Take that thing away, Willa Cather! And don't come around asking silly questions. Just study your lessons and please learn to sit still in class." His hand shook as he flipped the page of the book.

Willa moved sadly out of the room. He didn't know, she was sure. And how would she ever learn? She was so deep in thought that she did not notice the principal passing through the hall.

But that afternoon as she marched out of the schoolhouse with her classmates, Mrs. Goudy drew her aside.

"Willa," she said softly so that no one else heard her, "do you know Mr. Ducker? Uncle William Ducker, people call him."

"Why—why yes, ma'am. I mean, I know who he is. He helps in his brother's store, doesn't he?"

The principal nodded. "I just thought you might not know that he is an interesting man. He knows about all sorts of things—like goldenrod, for instance—and other things, too."

She gave Willa a special smile and then made a place for her in the marching line before she could say another word.

As she walked away from the school, Willa's head buzzed with questions while her friends laughed and chattered around her. When they reached Ducker's Store, she dropped behind and then stepped into the doorway. This was a time to be alone.

At first, in the dim light, she thought she was the only person in the store. Then she looked to her left and there was Uncle William, as everyone called him. His head rested on his hands; a book lay open on the counter before him. As he read, he twisted a thin lock of hair that fell over his eyes.

Willa tiptoed across the floor, trying not to startle him. When she reached the counter she peered cautiously at the book, for she wanted to see if it was anything she had read.

But what kind of book was that? It was not English, nor even French. It was not German either, she decided, but she moved closer just to be sure.

"Can you read it upside down, Miss Willa?" a gentle voice asked. "Or shall I turn it around?"

Willa looked directly into two twinkling blue eyes.

"My father says you're an Englishman. Do they read that kind of writing in England?" Willa asked.

Uncle William rubbed a hand affectionately across the page. "Some people do," he answered.

"What is it? The writing, I mean," she persisted until he saw that she was serious.

He turned the book around for her to see.

"It is an old, old story written in Greek by a man named Homer. It is called the *Iliad*." And then, seeing the yearning on her face, he went on to tell the exciting story and to read a little in the strange language.

When two customers finally came in, Willa wandered out through the alley door, her thoughts whirling among Greek warriors and gods and beautiful women; and especially her mind dwelt on the wrathful Achilles. She was nearly home before she remembered the goldenrod.

The next day, directly after school, she took a sprig of the wild flower to Uncle William and watched his face carefully as she laid it in front of him.

"Hmmmm," he said, slowly pulling a small magnifying glass from his vest pocket. *"Solidago memoralis,* commonly called goldenrod. There are a number of varieties, you know," he went on as though he were talking to himself. "But this is an especially fine specimen." He handed the glass to her.

Willa held the glass as he had, and there before her was a tiny blossom enlarged so that she could see the parts easily—the petals, the masses of pollen—

"Oh-h-h" she breathed. "Now I know why Mrs. Goudy asked me if I knew you."

Mr. Ducker stared at her, trying to read what was behind that smooth, wide forehead and those eager blue eyes. And then a look of happiness spread over his lean, serious face as though he, too, had found what he had been looking for.

He glanced furtively across the room at his brother who was unpacking a barrel of new merchandise.

"Come on," he whispered. "We can skip out for a minute."

Like two mischievous children, they tiptoed out the back way. With an air of mystery he unlocked the door of a small shed. Inside, he opened the heavy curtains that covered the window.

"My laboratory," he said. "I work here whenever I can. There are so many things to find out in this Nebraska of yours. The flowers—many are different from those I knew in England. And even the animals—why, these jack rabbits are huge."

All the time he was talking, Willa scanned the shelves and table, with their mysterious bottles, each one carefully labeled; the homemade alcohol lamps; the books in neat rows. But when he mentioned the rabbits her heart skipped a beat.

"Animals, too?" she gasped. "Oh, will you teach me?"

Slowly he shook his head. "No, but I will help you to find out for yourself. One thing at a time. You search carefully for the answer and then, when you find it, it belongs to you. That is the only way for a mind like yours."

He took a book from a shelf and covered it carefully with wrapping paper. "This is the *Iliad,* in English. First, you will want to know Latin—and then Greek, later. And on Saturdays, come here if you like. I will show you how to start looking for what you want to find."

That night Willa lighted the lamp next to her bed and locked the door of her new bedroom. With a little shiver of expectation she pulled the book from under her mattress, climbed into bed, and drew the covers up to her chin.

But before she began to read she looked up at the new wallpaper that she had selected. Bess thought she should have the big red rose pattern because it was so cheerful-looking. But she had insisted upon the wild roses. Uncle William would know the Latin name for them. He would show her how to find it in one of his books.

CHAPTER ELEVEN

THE bond between Willa and Uncle William Ducker continued to grow, for they had one thing in common —a desire to learn. No question was too small or too large. Sometimes they could not find the answer, but they never hesitated to try.

"What is this?" Willa might ask, bringing in one of her pressed flowers for Uncle William to see. A gleam would come into his eyes, and he would point to a book on his shelves. That was a signal for questions and answers that might lead to a discussion on any subject: the conjugation of Latin verbs, or perhaps the age of Julius Caesar and why he fought the Gauls.

Or Willa would reach into her sweater pocket and bring out a frog that she had caught near an ice-crusted swamp. "It feels warm," she might say. "Does it have blood like ours?" That would take them to the microscope that Uncle William had carried all the way from England.

Nebraska was full of interesting people: the immigrants who had first opened the world to her, Professor Shindelmeisser and his wonderful life among musicians. And now Uncle William was helping her along a new, uncharted path.

Dutifully she recited her lessons in the natural science class, wishing that she could help the struggling teacher but knowing that she dared not try.

And then one Saturday her mother, who had been ill, sent Roscoe for Dr. McKeeby. Willa slipped into the bedroom with the doctor and sat quietly in a corner. The curing of the sick was another mystery that intrigued her, but Uncle William had no medical books.

She watched while the handsome, distinguished-looking doctor took a thermometer from his small black bag, slipped it into her mother's mouth, and then gently pressed the artery in her wrist. Willa tried to breathe softly while he gazed at his big gold watch and counted the pulse beats. This was very important, she knew, determined to find out if she could do it.

I could take Roscoe's pulse if he'd let me, she thought. And Grandma's and Margie's and Mary's and maybe even some of the cats'!

"You must stay in bed, Mrs. Cather," she heard the doctor say gently as he placed a bottle of dark medicine on the dresser. "And take one teaspoon of this every four hours. I'll come in to see you again tomorrow."

The doctor had wonderful medicines that would cure anything! Her mother sounded better already.

"Oh, *thank* you, Doctor," she said. "Willa, maybe Margie has a little something for Dr. McKeeby in the kitchen."

Willa led the way and put a chair in a sunny spot at the table, where Margie had already set out a piece of pumpkin pie. She lifted the big coffee pot from the stove.

"Does everyone have a pulse?" she asked abruptly before anyone could come in to stop her. "I mean, all the people and horses and cows and—"

He smiled at her eager, intense face, and then he answered soberly. "Everything that has a heart must have a pulse. You see, when the heart beats—"

"Oh, *now* I understand," she cried, her mind racing ahead of his words. "But Uncle William doesn't have any medical books."

"Uncle William Ducker? You've been reading his books? What else do you read?"

"Oh, lots of things at the Weiners'. And sometimes Mrs. Miner gets a new book that she lets me see."

The doctor stroked his mustache thoughtfully. "Medical books are different," he said kindly. "The words are hard to understand. Many of them are in Latin."

"I can read some Latin. Uncle William hears me nearly every day, and I can work even harder if—"

The doctor finished his pie and rose to leave, adjusting the neatly folded handkerchief in his breast pocket as he gave her last remarks some thought. Willa looked on admiringly. Besides her father and Mr. Miner, Dr. McKeeby was the most distinguished-looking man in town, she had long ago decided. In addition, he had an air of a large city about him, of places and ways that existed only in her imagination.

Playfully he ran his fingers all around the crown of her head. "There seem to be some extra spaces here that need to be filled," he said. And then he was serious. "Willa, the books are there in my office for you to see whenever you like. Besides, I like having you around. Don't wait for an invitation."

Willa wandered back into the bedroom. Her mother

turned her head when her daughter came in. She seemed wider awake now.

"Do you feel better, Mother?" Willa asked.

"Yes. Dr. McKeeby always does something for me. It's the ways he looks and acts, I sometimes think, more than the medicine."

Then she sighed. "Willa, I do wish you could see how important it is to take care of yourself. Your hair is a sight. I do believe you haven't brushed it since I've been ill. Why can't you look trim and neat, like Dr. McKeeby?"

Willa put a hand to her matted hair. How she hated curls! She had endured them for years to please her mother. But now—

"I—I'm glad you're better," she said, edging toward the door. "Maybe you can go to sleep."

As soon as she was outside she began to run before she lost her courage. It took only a minute to reach the barber shop just off Webster Street. The barber was alone today. Her heart pounded as she slipped into the chair.

"A haircut, please," she said.

"Why, Willie Cather, you want me to cut off your curls? What will your mother say?" the barber objected.

Willa dug down in her pocket and pulled out the

ten-cent piece she had been saving since her birthday.

"She says my hair's a sight. She wants me to look like Dr. McKeeby."

"You want it real short like that?"

Willa nodded, shut her eyes, and settled down to silence. She didn't want to talk or he might decide not to cut it at all. Her mother would like her hair when she got used to it. And how could she study to be a doctor if she had curls?

When at last the barber said, "Well, there you are," she stood up and looked into the mirror. A strange boy stared back at her. He had her nose and eyes and chin.

Gradually a broad smile spread over the reflected face.

"That's just right," Willa cried. "It's just like Dr. McKeeby's."

She ran down the street, oblivious to the stares of people she passed. She was a strange boy in girl's clothes —until they took a second look. And then she was just Willie Cather who was always up to something.

At first her mother wept when she saw her. But gradually she accepted Willa's hair just as she accepted everything else her daughter did, since there was little she could do about it anyway.

The short hair was a symbol to Willa. She was now Willie Cather, M.D., or better still—Dr. Will. On cold days, after she left Uncle William, she often curled up in a corner of Dr. McKeeby's office to pore over his books.

Or, if she was lucky, she might catch Dr. Damerell, the elderly country doctor, as he started out of town to see a patient. Willa had always had a special place in her heart for him since the day when he had told Henry Lambrecht he would not die from the snake bite.

"Well, Dr. Will," he would say. "Mrs. Sorensen is poorly today. She might need two doctors this time."

Then he would make a place beside him in his old black buggy and throw a dusty buffalo robe over her knees.

These were wonderful trips for Willa, for Dr. Damerell loved to talk. As they jogged by each house he would tell of the times he had been called there, and what the ailments were in that household.

"There's Grandma Erickson," he would say whenever he saw a certain stooped little figure in a long black dress and bonnet. "Out carrying water from the well while her big grandsons are playing in the barn, I'll wager. That bad knee'll give her trouble till she heeds my words. I've told her to put a good hot poultice on it and stay abed till the swelling goes."

Then Grandma would wave as though she knew just what he was saying, and hobble back into the house.

Everyone for miles around knew Dr. Damerell and

loved him. Even the newest immigrants soon recognized his old black buggy as it made its rounds, and waved to him from the fields.

Late one afternoon in spring, he and Willa drove back toward town after stopping to see how the Petersons' twin boys were doing. It was a day much like the one when Willa had arrived with her family from Virginia. The wind blew steadily from the southwest. There was that same delicious scent in the air that she knew she would recognize if she came upon it anywhere in the world.

"Wild plum blossoms," she sighed.

"Yes, I always wait for them each spring," the doctor said, as if he read her thoughts. "They have a special meaning to these poor people in their soddies: the end of cold and misery for another year; the beginning of growth, of hope for a good harvest, of food for another long winter."

"Like the Sadileks," Willa said. "I always miss Annie most when spring comes. She was my first friend in Nebraska."

They jogged along in silence for a while, thinking of other times. Willa was about to ask if he remembered Henry Lambrecht's snake bite, when suddenly a shrill sound broke their reverie.

"Doctor! Doctor!" a child's voice screamed in the

distance. Then, "Doctor! Doctor!" it came again, closer now.

Willa leaned out of the buggy to scan the horizon, while the doctor pulled on the reins. At last they saw a small boy racing across the field.

Quickly the doctor turned his horse into a narrow lane and cracked his whip. Something was wrong in the soddie ahead. He did not need an explanation—the frantic cry of a small boy sent to intercept him was a familiar one.

A man stood in the doorway of the dark sod house holding a lantern. Behind him, a boy moaned and cried out in agony. The doctor brushed past the father and Willa followed on his heels.

On a pallet of straw in the corner, under a glaring lantern, a young boy writhed while a white-faced woman knelt beside him wringing her hands and uttering a frantic prayer in a foreign tongue. Two children stared in wide-eyed terror from the corner.

Dr. Damerell took a quick look and ordered the woman and children from the house. Then he put a hand on Willa's shoulder. "You can go, too, Willie. It's going to be pretty bad. Foot's crushed."

"But don't you need me? You can't do everything alone." She stood her ground, her feet planted firmly.

He gave her a long look, and then he bent his head

over his bag. "Your mother won't like this when she hears about it, but I could sure use a good steady helper." He took a small bottle from his bag and held it out to her. "Here you are, Dr. Will. Give him just enough sniffs of this to put him to sleep—no more, mind you. And see that you don't get your own nose into it. One patient's enough!" he said tersely.

Willa felt her hand shake as she took the bottle from him. She hoped he didn't notice. She wasn't afraid, but this was the first time she had been able really to help. All the rest had been make-believe.

Gingerly she pulled out the cork, turned the boy's head to one side, and held the bottle near his nose. He twisted and gasped, but she tried again.

"Easy now," the doctor cautioned. "Keep that cork in when you can or we'll all get dizzy."

"Emil," he called to the stolid father. "Give me a hand."

Together the two men gently lifted the moaning boy onto the table. While the father adjusted the lantern and stirred the fire in the stove, Willa went on with her job. Soon the boy stopped tossing his damp mop of hair from side to side. She watched the eyelids flutter in the pale, freckled face. And then his lips parted slightly, and he seemed to drop into slumber. The little bottle had worked a miracle!

"Willie, keep your eyes on his face," the doctor ordered sharply. His shirt sleeves were rolled up now, and Willa caught a glint of perspiration on his forehead under the glaring lamp. She heard a sound like a saw rasping through bone, but she did not look up. She gritted her teeth and tried not to think of what was going on. Dr. Damerell had his work to do and she had hers.

At last, as if from a distance, she heard the doctor say, "Good girl, Willie. That's all. Better get outside for some air."

Willa felt her way outside and sank down on the doorstep. Her head was spinning from the fumes, the heat from the stove, and the knowledge of what had gone on in that house. But she held her chin high and took deep breaths of the soft spring air.

When the doctor joined her and they got into the buggy, it was nearly dark. She shivered a little and pulled the robe up around her, even though it was a warm evening. For a while they rode in silence.

At last Dr. Damerell spoke. "I'll have to explain to your mother and father," he said. "They're bound to hear about this."

"Oh, you needn't. They never stop me—didn't you know? Mother always says she guesses I just have to learn any way I can in Red Cloud."

And then abruptly she asked the question that had been nagging at her mind.

"What would have happened if you hadn't cut it off?"

"The foot was no good to him," the doctor explained as kindly as he could. "When you see something like that, Dr. Will, you know what you have to do. It's a chance for life, or sure death. There was no question today."

Willa sighed deeply and leaned back against the hard cushion. The stars were coming out now, one by one. They winked at her as if to say that all was well again.

"Life or death," she murmured. A doctor makes the difference. "If you hadn't been there— Oh, it must be wonderful to be a doctor!"

Her gray-haired companion looked at her quizzically in the lantern light. "You seem to be getting serious about doctoring," he said. "But I thought you were going to be a literary lady. Everybody says you read all kinds of books—even Latin and Greek—with Uncle William Ducker. And Mrs. Weiner told me you're learning French."

Willa nodded and then she sighed again, a deep sigh that seemed to come from her very toes.

"Oh, there are so many interesting things to be! I

want to be everything and read everything and see everything!"

Dr. Damerell cracked his whip lightly over the plodding old horse.

"But today you want to be a doctor—and next year you may want to be something else." He nodded approvingly. "That is as it should be. Look at the world with a broad view before you make up your mind. And then someday you will not need to decide—you will *know*."

CHAPTER TWELVE

"DAUGHTER, what do you do all day?" Willa's father asked one morning during her fifteenth summer as she strode along beside him toward his loan and insurance office. "Your mother says you're never at home and I've been hearing all sorts of tales about you. Somebody said he saw you carrying a dead cat under your arm the other night. Where were you going with it?"

Willa looked up at her kind, patient father. He had never really scolded her, not even for cutting her hair, though she knew he had always admired her red-brown curls and must have been shocked. Their fair skin and deep blue eyes were the same, but in every other way they were different. Perhaps that was why she loved him so much.

"Nothing you are ashamed of, I hope," he went on, gently chiding her.

"Oh, no!" she denied quickly. "I just had to have it for an experiment. Uncle William Ducker and I are studying the circulatory system of animals, and we've been looking for a cat."

"To cut up?" Mr. Cather exclaimed. "No wonder people are talking!"

"Well, let them talk then! How else can we find out? I can't learn at school except from some old pictures."

"But why do you want to know?" He was truly puzzled.

Willa walked along for a while, kicking a pebble with the toe of a scuffed shoe. How could she tell him when she didn't really know herself?

"I—I don't know," she admitted at last. "I just have to find out, that's all. There's something inside me that makes me want to know everything in the world!"

"Everything in Red Cloud, you mean?"

"Everything here, first, and then later—" Her voice trailed off, troubled.

"Like the things you learned from Professor Shindelmeisser?"

She nodded. "And from Uncle William and the doctors and Mrs. Weiner. And from just looking and feeling and smelling—and thinking."

Mr. Cather smiled indulgently and patted her hand.
"I see," he said.

He didn't really see, Willa knew. But he wouldn't
try to stop her.

They were nearing his little office now. He seemed to
have more that he wanted to say.

"You used to feel this same way about the immigrants and all the places around Catherton. Have you
forgotten?"

"Forgotten? How could I forget?" she asked,
shocked that he might think she could. "I remember
every face and name and story! Why, sometimes at
night, even in winter, I think I can smell the fresh-cut
hay in Grandfather's pasture. And last summer when I
couldn't go back because Mother was sick, I thought I
couldn't stand it not to ride along the sunflower trails
with Annie or Leedy."

Big as she was—almost up to her tall father's shoulder—she felt hot tears sting her eyes. She had never
talked quite like this to anyone before.

"Hmm," her father commented. "Well, then you'd better make some plans with Grandfather Cather for this summer. He sent word yesterday with one of the neighbors that he'd be in town today."

"He did? And Grandmother, too?"

"No," her father replied. But when he said good-by there was that old twinkle in his eyes that made her wonder.

Aimlessly, Willa wandered on down the street, and then east toward the Crooked Creek bridge. She had intended to go to the laboratory first, but the conversation with her father had sent her mind in other directions.

The laboratory was better in winter, she decided, when no warm wind called her to come listen to the rustle of cottonwood leaves in Captain Garber's grove. She wandered on across the bridge and into the depth of the grove, near the site of the first stockade. A big house stood on the hill now, since the captain had been governor of the state and had returned with his beautiful young wife to live in Red Cloud. But Willa liked to think of him as the captain who had ventured into this Indian territory and had established the town.

She threw herself down under one of the tallest trees and looked up into the shimmering leaves that never seemed to be still. The slightest breeze would start them whispering to each other. For a long time she lay there, hearing at the same time the rustle of the tall red grass up in the Catherton country. And then she rolled over and pulled a book from her pocket.

It was a story that Mrs. Weiner had let her take, written by a Frenchman named Flaubert. Mrs. Weiner, who had traveled in France, said that Nebraska sometimes reminded her of certain parts of that country. Someday she would just *have* to find out for herself.

But it was hard to concentrate on reading when she kept seeing that twinkle in her father's eyes. It could even be that Grandfather had started before daybreak to avoid the heat. What if he should arrive when she was gone?

Restlessly she got up again and wandered back into town. She could go by her house, just to see, and then on to the Miners'. But as she neared home, she suddenly remembered that this was Tuesday and Mary would be having her lesson. Besides, something mysterious had been going on when Mary practiced. There seemed to be a big secret that only Professor Shindelmeisser and Mary and her mother shared.

Willa had stopped her piano lessons when she entered high school, but she often walked along with the little professor after he left the Miners'. They had become fast friends, but lately he seemed to be avoiding her, especially since she had tried to pry the secret from him.

So there was nothing to do but go up to her room and wait for the rumble of the big wagon.

Just before noon, when she was becoming a little bored with the antics of the heroine in her French novel, she heard the wagon rattling along the street. It was such a big wagon that it had a special sound of its own.

Willa threw her book aside and raced down the stairs. It was always wonderful to see Grandfather again. And maybe Grandmother would be with him after all.

She ran out the back door, expecting him to pull up at the rear as he usually did. But to her astonishment, he passed on by the house as if he had forgotten where they lived. And who could that be on the seat beside him?

Willa tore after the wagon trying to see. It was a young woman. She was dressed in a neat country waist and skirt, and her head was bare. But there was something about the regal way that she carried her head on her shoulders—

"Annie! Annie Sadilek!" Willa screamed as the wagon drew up at the Miners'.

Though she looked so different, it was the same Annie who laughed and cried and hugged Willa after she stepped down from the wagon seat.

"Willie! Little Willie!" she exclaimed, daubing at her moist brown eyes and running her hand over Willa's short hair. "So grown up."

And then she turned and smoothed her skirt with her sun-browned, calloused hands as Mrs. Miner and the children came down the walk.

Willa stared in amazement as Mrs. Miner greeted Annie warmly and the children helped carry the bundles into the house. What was Annie doing here in town? And at the Miners'?

She looked to Grandfather for an answer.

"Your Grandmother and I will miss Annie now that she's here to work for the Miners. Will you come out to see us soon?"

So that was why! Willa nodded and squeezed his hand. "The next time you come to town, maybe I can go back with you. The sunflowers will be out then. And I want to see everybody—Grandmother and the Lambrechts and Boots and. . . . But Annie's here now. Why did she leave the country?"

Grandfather's bright blue eyes clouded. "Times have been hard for that family," he said, shaking his head. "She's going to work here and send her money home to help. That old dugout's not fit for another winter without a new window and door and a good stove. And somebody's got to buy the sugar and coffee.

"Annie's a good worker," he went on. "But it's not been right—her doing a man's work all day. You be good to her, Willie."

"Oh, yes!" Willa promised. How could anyone *not* be good to Annie?

As often as she could, Willa went over to the Miners' to visit her old friend, who quickly made a place for herself in that happy household. She could never seem to do enough. No matter how much she had washed and ironed and scrubbed during the day, she would always be ready to pop corn or make taffy in the evening for all the children. And she laughed a great deal now, as she did when she first came to Nebraska. Sometimes, when Willa played charades in the big warm kitchen, rich with the smell of boiling molasses taffy, she felt that she had gone back five years to an evening at the farm.

But on other days she felt like a stranger. For Annie had been told the secret, too. She guarded the house when Mary practiced, as though she were Mary's friend instead of Willa's. No amount of questioning would ferret out the answer.

"You just wait, Willie," she would say. "Soon now you know."

Many times, Willa turned away frustrated, unable to go on with anything that she usually liked to do—not able even to enjoy a ride into the country with Dr. Damerell. The Mexican music from across the tracks failed to excite her.

And then one day Father came home to dinner bursting with the news.

"Have you heard?" he announced, though he knew they hadn't. "Blind Boone is coming to town! And Mary Miner is going to play the secret piano piece. Shindelmeisser has one for her that he thinks *no* one will know, not even Boone."

"What's she agoin' to do that for?" Margie asked as she dished up the applesauce.

While Father tried to explain to Margie and the younger children, Willa's mind raced through what she had heard about the blind man who drew such sweet music from the piano. The traveling salesmen who sat out in front of the hotel on hot evenings often talked about him. He could play anything—anything at all.

But the high moment of each performance came when someone from the audience walked up on the stage and played a selection that Blind Boone supposedly did not know. He would listen intently, rocking back and forth all the while, and then he would play it right off from memory.

"Just like that," the salesmen would say, even though no one really believed them. Everyone knew it took months to learn a difficult piece. Why, even Mary Miner, who played better than any other girl in town, practiced for hours every day.

But now they were going to find out!

Willa caught herself humming a phrase that she had heard faintly at times when she went past the Miners'. And then she clapped her hand over her mouth. Nobody was going to learn the melody from *her*.

"Poor li'l old man," Margie said when Father finished his careful explanation. "Mary Miner's playin' a bad trick on him. It's sinful, that's what it is."

For several days Margie treated Mary coldly whenever she came into the Cather kitchen. But to Willa and Annie and the whole population of Red Cloud, Mary was a heroine.

On Saturday night everyone except Margie dressed in his best clothes and went up to the opera house. Mrs. Miner helped Annie make over one of her own striped silk dresses and bought a ticket for her. When Willa walked into the Miners' kitchen that night and saw the little immigrant girl transformed into a glowing young woman, she gasped.

"All the boys in town will be staring at you tonight, Annie," she warned.

Annie looked into the mirror over the washstand and

smiled to herself. Then she tossed her head as though she already knew that they would.

Every seat in the opera house was taken, and late comers stood around the walls. Mrs. Holland sat in the front row, looking important, as usual, and wearing her diamonds. A rumor had flown through town before supper that Boone had played a special concert for her in the hotel. But all outsiders had been barred, so no one was sure.

People craned their necks to look from Mrs. Holland to Mary Miner, who sat on the other side of the aisle. She wore a new pink silk dress and held her leather music case on her lap. But there were some in the audience who stared at the handsome young woman seated between Mrs. Miner and Willa. Annie's smooth brown cheeks were flushed with excitement and her brown eyes darted here and there, full of golden lights.

Suddenly a hush came over everyone, the house lights went out, and Willa felt Annie's hand creep trustingly into hers. Applause thundered through the hall as Mr. Miner stepped out onto the stage with a short, round little man.

Willa stared, amazed, as they walked slowly across the stage. So this was Blind Boone! Beside Mr. Miner he probably appeared shorter than he really was. His little, close-cropped head seemed to rest in rolls of flesh above a gleaming white collar. And the tails of his coat dangled below his knees.

But as soon as he reached the piano and Mr. Miner left, Willa forgot how he looked. She scarcely noticed the sunken, sightless eyes. She saw only the happy, glowing face that nodded toward the packed auditorium and the restless fingers that stroked the piano lovingly.

Then he sat down on the piano stool and ran his fingers lightly back and forth across the keys, nodding his head over them as if he were whispering sweet thoughts. There was not a sound in the room except the pounding of Willa's heart when he struck the first notes.

The piano laughed and sang and thundered and sobbed that night. Willa did not know what he played— nor did she care. Sometimes she caught snatches of melodies that she had heard. But for her, as for many others in the audience, the piano came to life as it never had before, even when Professor Shindelmeisser played.

It's like a real person to him, she thought as she watched him sway back and forth in rhythm. He's making it laugh now because he's happy. And sometimes he thinks sad thoughts and makes it cry.

Then suddenly he stood up and bowed again and again, until the applause dwindled away.

Now it was time for Mary! Mr. Miner escorted Blind Boone to a chair at the side of the stage and then explained to the audience what would come next, just as though there was anyone in Red Cloud who didn't know. Someone in the audience, he said, would play a piano selection. Mr. Boone would listen to it just once, and then he would play it from memory.

All eyes followed Mary as she walked sedately across the stage, sat down at the piano, and calmly placed her music on the rack. She didn't seem nervous at all, Willa thought, squeezing Annie's hand hard. But then Mary never did fidget.

A group of traveling salesmen in the second row turned to smile smugly. Maybe *now* the people of Red Cloud would believe them.

No one moved while Mary skillfully played through a difficult number, full of runs and chords from beginning to end. How could anyone memorize such a piece in a few minutes when Mary had been practicing it for months? Yet Willa sensed that all the people in that crowded hall wanted to believe this man could. He wasn't like other people. He *was* music—nothing else —just music. If anyone could do it, he could.

When Mary finished and the blind musician took her place at the piano, no one moved. Even the smallest boys sat paralyzed, waiting, while he touched a key softly, then another, and hummed a few notes as though he were alone in the room.

Suddenly he began to play—slowly at first, and then faster and faster, as though the music were coursing through his veins and out through his very fingertips. It *was* Mary's piece; no one could mistake it! The audience sat awestruck until he reached the end, and then in a body they rose and cheered and clapped. They would not let him leave the stage until he had given them one encore after another.

At last he slipped into "Home, Sweet Home," played so hauntingly that the crowd let him go.

As they filed up the aisle, Willa noticed tears in Annie's eyes. Her friend clung to her, speechless, until they were out in the clear night air.

"Willie," she finally said in a husky voice, "my papa would have liked that music. In Bohemia we heard much music like that—from the heart. Someday maybe you go there to hear it, too?"

How could Annie have known what she had been thinking? The world must be full of music that moved people, made them want to cry or to dance from joy. Someday she would go where that music was—if it was all the way to Bohemia!

CHAPTER THIRTEEN

THE huge golden sunflowers were in full bloom when Willa and Roscoe drove out toward the farm one Sunday with Grandfather. The corn stood tall in the fields. Everywhere more ground had been broken for corn or grain, until the country was becoming a huge checkerboard of colors—green and yellow and brown. The tawny grass that had rolled in uninterrupted waves across the prairie was giving way to the plow.

While Grandfather and Roscoe talked about the crops and the hail that had threatened the wheat at the end of a breathless day in July, Willa rode in silence.

The fierce sun beat down upon her, but she scarcely noticed. Her eyes roved everywhere looking for old landmarks—the things she loved and remembered. Where was the swamp that turned into a pond after heavy rains? Wild geese always stopped there in the fall. If she closed her eyes she could still hear their eerie honking as they signaled each other.

A lone duck flew up from the roadside and she watched its flight, remembering how often wings of wild fowl had whirred above her head when she rode over the prairie. Now the farmers complained about how much grain the birds consumed each year, Grandfather said.

"Well, Willie, are you glad to come back? Or will you miss the town and all the people?" Grandfather smiled at her as he spoke, and Willa noted some new lines around his eyes. Even *he* was changing.

"Oh, yes," she said, rousing herself from her daydream. "But everything looks different. How could so much happen in only two years?"

Grandfather threw back his head and laughed in the old, familiar way. At least his laugh was the same.

"Why, Willie, everything changes—that's progress, people say. Even *you* have changed, you know." He reached across Roscoe to ruffle her short-cropped hair. "Your grandmother and I like having more neighbors—

we like to see them get better houses and more comforts as they grow older, too. Don't you?"

"Yes, but—but the land. It was so wonderful and wild and exciting. No! I don't want it to change!" she ended fiercely.

Grandfather nodded. "I know what you mean. Well, Boots is waiting to ride out toward the west and north. It's not so different there, you'll see. The dog-town is still flourishing, and there are plenty of rattlesnakes!"

Willa laughed and felt better at once. Of course there wouldn't be anyone living near the dog-town—not until all the more fertile land had been taken up. And she could go farther north this time, past the French settlement to country she had never seen.

For two weeks, Willa tried to turn back the clock to the days when Catherton was the wide world. Mrs. Lambrecht baked *Streuselkuchen* for her and Henry brought out his collection of snake rattles. She examined each one of the bony pieces as though she had never seen them before and admired the new ones. In the evenings Henry played his harmonica for her; but some of the selections were new ones he had picked up in town, and the old ones did not seem so wonderful as she remembered them, no matter how hard she tried to believe they were.

When she asked to carry the mail again, Grandfather

shook his head. "There are too many new people, Willie," he said. "You'd never find them all. Besides, there's a regular mailman now—a new fellow sent down from Hastings."

But there were happy, satisfying days, too—like the morning when she and Roscoe rode up to the dog-town. The little animals sunned themselves on their mounds of earth, unaware of that thing Grandfather called "progress." They sat on their hind legs, barked in the same outraged tones, and then scurried underground.

Willa laughed in delight and patted Boots, who pranced nervously and tossed his head from side to side. "You remember, too, don't you?" she said, and her heart beat faster as she recalled the ugly flat head of the rattler that had struck Henry on that other summer day.

On the way back home, they circled down along the draw, avoiding the curling copper-colored leaves of the smartweed as they used to do. The rank odor of decaying ironweed in the swampy draw touched Willa's senses like a familiar perfume. She raised her head to sniff it again.

Suddenly she gave a triumphant cry and dug a bare heel into Boots's flank.

"Look!" she called to Roscoe who had wandered off onto firmer ground. Her pony raced across the draw to the field beyond and pulled up sharply at a tug on the reins.

There, almost under Boots's prancing hoofs, was something Willa had been looking for ever since her very first summer at the farm. A clump of rare orange milkweed gleamed like a basket of real oranges in the close-cropped green field.

She dropped to her knees and clawed into the rich earth with her bare hands to get it all. When Roscoe came up to her, he saw tears streaming down her face.

"Why, Willie, what's the matter? It's just an old milkweed," he said, nonplused.

Willa wiped the tears from her face with her shirt sleeve. And then she pulled a large red handkerchief from her pocket and gently lifted the precious plant into it, careful not to disturb the roots.

"I know it's silly," she answered shamefacedly. "But everything's being plowed up—all the beautiful wild flowers and grass—until pretty soon there won't be any left." She held the plant gently in one arm and slid onto Boots's back again. "But now I'll have this for my collection, and I can remember every time I see it, even years and years from now."

On their last night at the farm, Willa tossed restlessly in the little attic room where she had spent her first night in Nebraska. The air was close and still; the bed sheets, steamy from the day-long heat of a fierce sun, seemed to blister her moist skin. For a while she lay on her side and watched heat lightning flutter on the horizon while disturbing thoughts roved through her mind. For lately a war had been going on within her.

Nebraska meant more to her than it did to anyone she knew. The bountiful flowers of every hue; the wild grass; the whispering cottonwood trees that shimmered in the hot, brilliant sun; even the leaden winters that held the secret of next year's abundance—no one else loved it as she did!

Then why did she want to go away? There was the whole world to explore—music to hear; books, great libraries of them, to read. She *had* to go! And yet, when she came back, nothing would be the same at all.

There was no answer for her here in this room with all its memories.

Impatiently she slipped out of bed and pulled on an old shirt and pair of trousers. The sky, too, was restless tonight. Perhaps it did not like what was going on here, either.

Quietly she crept down the stairs. Roscoe's bed creaked as she passed his open door and a great rumbling snore rolled from her grandparents' room.

She ambled out to the tall windmill, leaned against it, and looked up through the huge blades at the top. A light breeze caught and gently turned them; they creaked mournfully on their axis. There was nothing between her and the brittle stars overhead except the great, stark wheel that painfully cut its way through the air.

Suddenly Willa grasped a rung of the windmill ladder. Up and up she climbed, closer and closer to those inscrutable stars.

Halfway to the top she heard a faint, distant rumble and clung to the ladder while she looked around. From the east, a mass of boiling thunderheads moved relentlessly across each constellation. As she watched, fascinated, they seemed to take on a fresh burst of speed. Suddenly a great orange flash split the arc overhead, turning the night sky to a deep, fathomless blue. The earth below her—the cornstalks, the fence rails, the winding road—changed to an eerie yellow for a moment and then was swallowed up in darkness. A thousand drums crashed a warning.

"Willie! Willie!" she heard Roscoe call just as a great gust of wind sent the giant wheel whirling above her.

If she hurried she could make the top before the next flash of lightning! On and on she climbed until her

· 145 ·

grasping hand could find no more rungs. She had reached the top! The roar of the frantic, whirling blades drowned out the pounding of her heart.

She threw back her head and looked toward the stars, but they were gone. Then a jagged gash of light cut through the boiling mass above her. Quickly her eyes searched in every direction. There were the houses, the winding road, the fields of her beloved country—more than she had ever seen at one time before—more than she might ever see again. They stood out, clear and luminous, and then they were gone in a gush of wind and rain and another deafening crash of thunder.

Slowly Willa felt her way down the ladder again. The rain beat against her face, but her heart was at peace.

When she reached the ground, Roscoe clung to her, his teeth chattering, while the storm moved away as quickly as it had come.

"Oh, Willie, weren't you *scared?*" he cried.

She put her arm around him and led him toward the house. "Scared? No, I—I guess I wasn't scared," she said truthfully. "It was such a beautiful storm."

CHAPTER FOURTEEN

AFTER Willa returned to Red Cloud, her mind was fully made up. She had only one more year of high school, and then she *must* go to college. How she was to accomplish this she did not know, but she just had to find a way.

She read more diligently than ever in the Weiners' library and talked to Mrs. Weiner often about her problem. Mrs. Weiner was as convinced as Willa that nothing must stop her.

"I will speak to your mother," she said. "What can you ever do here in Red Cloud?"

But Willa begged her to wait. Her father thought she should teach in a country school for a while, but perhaps he would change his mind. Her real concern was with her mother. Once Mrs. Cather's mind was made up, it remained that way. So far she had not said, one way or another. And Willa did not want to press her until the right moment came.

Perhaps if her mother understood how little she knew about arithmetic and how poorly she spelled . . . Well, maybe it would be best not to explain, after all. She would never use arithmetic, she was sure, and who could care about spelling when there were more interesting things to learn? Thus her thoughts ran.

But while she waited, there were other things to think about. In her wanderings, Willa returned more and more often to the Garbers' grove southeast of town, not far from the river. There was something fascinating about the life in that big house on the hill. The very manner and bearing of the dignified captain who had been Governor of Nebraska and of his beautiful wife, only half his age, stirred her imagination.

They seldom mingled with the people of Red Cloud or took part in the social life there. But often a private railroad car from Omaha or Denver would park on the siding, and important-looking people would stay overnight with the Garbers.

Then the house rang with merriment, and the hired girls carried stories into the town of the beautifully gowned women and distinguished-looking men who stayed there.

The life that went on in that house was different from anything Willa had ever experienced, and she longed to know more about it. For the men who came to visit the Garbers were pioneers, too. She had asked her father about them one morning as she strolled along with him to his office.

"They are railroad men—men who helped build the West, Daughter," he answered. "Would we have tried to come to Nebraska if there had been no railroads? The immigrants came after the tracks were laid, too. Of course we know that some people rode from the East in covered wagons, but they were only a few, actually. Someone had to have the vision to open up the West in a bigger way. The courage, too," he added.

So there were different ways to build a country, Willa thought. Some did it with vision; others, with dogged determination, like the Lambrechts and the Sadileks and the Russians on that stubborn soil to the northwest. But all had one thing in common—courage—or they did not survive.

"Like Grandma Boak?" Willa asked surprisingly. She had suddenly thought of her tired, uncomplaining little grandmother who left her large, comfortable home in Virginia, to sleep on a hard little bed next to their drab kitchen in Nebraska.

"Yes," Father answered, slowly stroking his chin. "Courage and loyalty. The qualities we admire in people take many forms. Captain Garber is a good man. He has done much for Nebraska."

After she left her father, Willa turned again toward the east. She carried a basket on her arm, for she had told Grandma Boak that she would bring home some wild grapes for jelly. But first, she suddenly decided, she would take some to the Garbers.

Once she had made up her mind, she rushed through the picking, not even stopping to admire the new autumn colors around her. Captain Garber always sat in his garden on sunny mornings since he had been ill, she had heard. She wanted to have a good look at the red granite sundial there, to see for herself how it could tell the time of day.

As Willa strode up the hill, her full basket on her arm, she heard voices in the garden. She hesitated for a moment, almost ready to turn back, but something within her prodded her on. These were "pioneers," her father had said. Hadn't she gone to see every pioneer around Catherton? Besides, her father told her that Captain Garber was a good man.

She tossed her head and moved into the magic circle of the rose garden.

There, bending over the captain, arranging a light cover across his knees, was the lovely lady whom people talked about but did not really know. The sun sparkled on her soft, reddish hair, and lighted the fragile, almost transparent flesh of her cheeks.

"Such a gorgeous day, my dear," Willa heard her say as she stretched her arms up toward the sun, lithe and graceful as a young girl. And then she saw Willa, standing just outside the shadow of the trees. She could not have missed the admiration in Willa's eyes; they regarded her with pure delight.

"Hello," she said in a friendly, casual tone. "Why, you've been picking some of those wonderful wild grapes down by the river! I've been promising Captain Garber that I would go down, myself, to get some for him."

The captain turned heavily in his chair to observe Willa. Even in the role of a semi-invalid, he was a commanding-looking man. She could imagine him on a horse, leading his men to this hill, perhaps planting a flag where the stockade was to be. No wonder he had been made governor!

"I picked them for you," Willa said hurriedly, extending her basket.

Graciously Mrs. Garber accepted the gift. She poured the frosty-purple fruit in a lavish heap on the table before the captain, and then caught up a bunch and held it high, between her and the sun.

"Look," she cried as the sunlight brought out the rich color of the fruit. "Did you ever see anything so beautiful?"

The captain's eyes moved from the grapes to his lovely wife. "Beautiful," he said, but Willa knew that he did not mean the grapes.

Shy in the face of this kind of admiration which she had never seen before, except on the stage, Willa turned away to look at the sundial. It was carved in a massive block of red granite, set on a boulder in the very center of the garden. The lines and markings stood out distinctly in the sunlight.

While she was studying it she heard a low chuckle from the captain. "You must be young Miss Cather—Charles Cather's daughter," he said.

Willa flushed. How could he know? "Yes," she said. "I guess I should have told you."

The captain smiled kindly. "No need, my dear. I've seen you with your father. And someone else told me that you've found out as much about Webster County as anyone here. The fault is ours," he added graciously as he watched the color subside in her cheeks. "Mrs.

Garber and I should know our townspeople better than we do."

Then he changed the subject abruptly. "Do you understand the sundial?"

Willa turned back to it and traced the line of shadow with her finger. "I'm not sure," she said thoughtfully. "When the shadow is here—"

Carefully the captain explained the markings without getting up from his chair. It was as though the pattern on the stone were engraved in his memory, too. His young wife chatted happily with both of them.

When Willa turned to pick up her basket, Mrs. Garber thanked her again. "You must come often," she said sincerely. "See how much better Captain Garber looks after talking with you?"

This was the beginning of another kind of friendship that Willa never forgot. Sometimes that fall she would find the captain alone in his garden, studying his late roses or just thinking. The slightest question would send his mind off along the trail that had first brought him to Red Cloud. Or his thoughts might move along the railroad bed that had bogged down in swamps and come up against mountains on its way to Colorado.

"See that red granite?" he said one day, pointing to the sundial. "That's the kind we blasted through to lay those tracks."

Though Willa gazed toward the hard red rock, she was seeing, instead, mountains of it in Colorado, glistening in the sun. Someday she would really see all that fabulous country, too.

Mrs. Garber often drove her back to town or out along the river road where they could look at the clay bluffs of the opposite shore. Willa never knew why the captain's wife liked to be with her. It may have been because she listened so eagerly or always asked the right questions. Mrs. Garber liked to tell about the gay parties that she had attended in Denver before the captain's illness. And Willa's face was a bright mirror for her descriptions, tossing back their gaiety for her to relive.

At Christmas time, Willa was even invited to a party in the big house, a fact that her mother was never able to understand. There were many more attractive girls in town who were not asked to meet the young people arriving from Denver. The house on Cedar Street was in constant agitation from her mother's planning and sewing and worrying.

"Your *hair*, Willa," her mother said bitterly as she adjusted a fold in the blue velvet dress she had been sewing on all week. "If you only had hair like Mary Miner's!"

Willa looked into the mirror and liked what she saw. "Well," she answered with a special toss of her head that she had seen Mrs. Garber use, "Mary hasn't been invited. So maybe Mrs. Garber isn't interested in people's hair."

Her mother shrugged her shoulders, helpless in the face of such logic.

Just then a hack from the livery stable drew up and the whole family poured out of the house to see Willa off. Her mother ran a hand over the worn seat and exclaimed in disgust.

"Filthy!" she said, snatching Margie's apron from her and polishing everything she could reach with it. "Now don't use one of those awful lap robes or you'll be covered with horse hair, mind you. Oh dear, no one would ever believe we used to have our own horses and carriage."

Willa settled herself for the ride across the frozen creek and up the hill. It *was* cold, but she didn't mind doing without the robe for such a short ride. It would have been nicer, of course, to walk and look up at the brilliant stars and think about the evening ahead of her, but her mother wouldn't hear of such a thing.

"A young lady does not walk out alone in the evening," she had declared flatly.

Why did this party suddenly make her a young lady? No one had ever stopped her from going out alone before.

As she turned to wave good-by to the family group huddled in the feeble circle of the carriage light, she saw the longing in her pretty mother's face. Her mother would have known just what to do and say on an evening like this. How she had loved the big parties and good times back in Virginia. The belle of the county, Grandma Boak always said. Just as the carriage pulled away, the surprising thought came to Willa that maybe her mother, too, was a "pioneer."

In no time at all the carriage wheels rumbled across the bridge. Soon she heard the big cottonwood trees creaking with cold overhead. Lights glittered in every window of the big house, and before she touched the knocker the captain himself opened the front door.

Willa blinked and stepped back in sudden fright at the spectacle of black frock coats and colorful evening dresses—pink, lavender, yellow—all sparkling with jewels. But the captain gently drew her in, took her coat, and offered her his arm.

"Come," he said. "We want our friends to know each other."

Instantly all the terror drained out of her and she became her old self again, confident and eager to see and hear something new.

Afterward, Willa tried to tell everyone what had gone on that evening. She could remember the details when anyone asked her—Mrs. Garber's long sparkling earrings and the matching necklace, neither of which dimmed the gay lights in her lovely eyes; the candles and gleaming silver and linen; the great roast turkey that Captain Garber carved so skillfully; the pleasant talk about music and travel and events.

But the thing hardest to explain was how she had felt. For although she had expected to be an outsider, all of these people accepted her from the very beginning. The captain graciously took her from one group to another and Mrs. Garber soon joined them, dropping little remarks about things they had done together. If anyone wondered about her short hair and homemade dress, no one showed the slightest sign. She was an intimate friend of the Garbers. That made her one of them.

The leisurely graciousness of that dinner, with its many courses, served so effortlessly, and the relaxed and happy conversation in the living room afterward gave Willa a confidence she had not known before. No matter where she might go after she left Red Cloud, she would never find anything better than this!

CHAPTER FIFTEEN

ON THE evening of June 5, 1890, the high school held
its graduation exercises in the opera house. There were
only three to graduate that year—Willa and two boys—
all seated uncomfortably on the stage.

Willa wore a ruffled white muslin dress, which her
mother considered proper attire for a sixteen-year-old
young lady. But her hair was still short, and under the
starched ruffles she knew that she was no different—
only a little older.

The townspeople knew it, too, she thought. Some
of them—those who were not her friends, who did not
understand her—had come to find out what she would

do this time. For the gossip had grown in that little town, especially since the day when she had brought a dead cat to the high school laboratory so that she could show everyone how interesting zoology could really be. No one had wanted to find out—not even the teacher, who had ordered her to remove "that thing" at once.

Now, she thought a little bitterly, this was supposed to be the happiest time of her life. But was it? Had all these people come to see her because this was an end instead of a beginning?

As someone played the piano and the audience ceased their fidgeting, Willa looked from one face to another. There were some unfriendly faces, she could see. But lined up in the front rows were those she loved. There was her whole family, even Margie Anderson. Though they might not always understand her, they respected her and did not interfere. For this she would always be grateful. Behind them sat Grandfather and Grandmother Cather and all the Lambrechts, who had driven the sixteen miles to town just for her.

Uncle William Ducker sat at one side, twisting his lock of hair as he always did when he was deep in thought. When she caught his eye, he stiffened his back and sent her an encouraging smile. He was the only person who, so far, had heard her commencement address.

The two doctors nodded to her, and Mrs. Miner's eyes twinkled a greeting. Near the back of the room, in a row of hired girls, all from immigrant families that she knew, Annie's worshipful eyes flashed a message of love and pride. And just as the music ceased, a little man in a worn coat and black hat slipped in through the door. Even Professor Shindelmeisser had not forgotten her!

Slowly the tension slipped from Willa. She felt her whole being relax as she recalled Uncle William's words when she had left him only a few hours before.

"The world is full of disapproving people, Willa," he had said kindly. "They criticize because they do not understand—or perhaps because they cannot. Tell these people, tonight, what you believe and why. And then get on with your business of living as you think best. There is little enough time."

Uncle William, in this town, was spoken of as "queer," she knew. But he still read his epic poetry with the same relish. And he would always search zealously into the unknown even if the whole world turned against him. Well, so would she!

When the music stopped, Mrs. Goudy said a few kind words about the three who were to receive their diplomas that night. Each was to give an "address" on a subject of his own choosing.

The first speaker strode arrogantly to the center of the stage to receive his applause. He announced his subject, "Self Advertising."

Willa listened while her classmate told his audience that "a man should blow his own trumpet"; that honesty does not pay; that generosity is foolishness. When he came to the idea that it is a mistake for a man to do his work well, that he will get farther if he will merely puff himself up, Willa's disgust was complete.

In that audience before her she saw heads nodding in approval. Were there really people in Red Cloud who thought this way? She had been so busy filling her own mind that she had avoided people who had nothing in theirs. Was this what Uncle William had tried to tell her? She cast an alarmed glance in his direction, but he sat with his head down, one hand shielding his eyes from the disgusting spectacle.

Willa clenched her moist hands until the applause died and the second speaker took his place. Anger coursed through her. She knew that her face was flushed and her knees were shaking.

At last Uncle William squared his shoulders and looked directly at her as though he were trying to tell her something. His words came to her as he had spoken them only a few hours before: "Tell these people what you believe and why. And then get on with your business of living. There is little enough time." This must be what he was trying to say again from where he sat in that audience.

Slowly the heat in her face subsided. Her hands and heart grew quiet. She did not even listen to the second boy speak on "New Times Demand New Measures and New Men." She did not have to listen to him now; she never would have to again.

At last when it was her turn, she stepped confidently to the front and announced her subject: "Superstition versus Investigation." All the people stared at her, waiting. She spoke in a clear, firm voice, answering all the sly looks, the gossip that flared up whenever she did anything not considered proper.

First she talked about the dark times in history, when superstition ruled the world. Then she spoke of the brighter times when men knew they must find the truth. She told about people who had continued to experiment, even though they suffered humiliation and even death.

"Scientific investigation is the hope of our age, as it must precede all progress," she said defiantly, "and yet upon every hand we hear the objections to its pursuit. The boy who spends his time among the stones and flowers is a trifler; and if he tries with bungling attempt to pierce the mystery of animal life, he is cruel." Out of all this struggle, much good had come, she said, and many lives had been saved. But she could not resist ending on a bitter note.

When she finished, her family and friends clapped long and hard to cover up the scattered applause in the rest of the house. Annie's hands, in the back of the room, were the last to be still. Margie's face rose out of the crowd, speaking her love and adoration. She had not understood a word of the speech, but Willa was always right, so it did not matter.

Mrs. Weiner was one of the first to reach her side. "It was magnificent!" she said. "I have certainly heard nothing to compare with it in this town." Then she squeezed Willa's hand and whispered, "I spoke to your mother and grandmothers this afternoon. I could not wait any longer."

There was a party ready for Willa when she reached home. Her friends came by to eat strawberries and ice cream made in the Miners' big freezer, and to tell her how wonderful she had been. But no one asked her what she would do now.

At last, when only the family remained and the younger children had been put to bed, Grandmother Cather placed an envelope in Willa's hand and then looked toward her son Charles. Willa's father stood up and cleared his throat.

"Daughter," he said solemnly, "you are still very young—only sixteen."

Willa's heart sank. He had been saying this all year, whenever she talked about going to college. A sob rose in her throat. She wanted to rush out through the open door into the blackness where she could be alone. She couldn't stand hearing it again—not tonight!

"But in some ways you are much older," he went on. "We know you want to go to the university at Lincoln, but the loan business is—is not prospering as I had hoped." He cleared his throat uncomfortably.

What was he trying to tell her? Didn't he know she *had* to go? What if she stayed here? What could she do? She wanted to scream out the words, but everyone was looking at her. She was supposed to be grown up now. "There is little enough time," she seemed to hear Uncle William Ducker say again.

"Fortunately," her father's voice continued, "a way has been found. Your Grandmother Cather has a little money put aside. She will help you get started and we will all try to—"

The scream that Willa had been suppressing came out in a choking sob. She threw her arms around her father, and then around her grandmother, while tears streamed down her face. Everybody began hugging someone else, as though the whole family were going to college instead of only Willa.

Nothing else mattered now—the hostile faces, the skimpy applause, the disapproving glances were all shoved into the darkest part of her mind. For now she could get on with the business of living her life as she thought best.

POSTSCRIPT

Willa Cather attacked her work at the university as she did everything else—with her whole being. But it was not until she saw one of her essays in print in the local newspaper that she understood what Dr. Damerell meant. She knew, on that day, that she must be a writer. She began to fill the pages of the college magazine with poems, articles, and short stories. Her love of plays and music led her to the theater; following each performance she wrote her opinions for the State Journal.

After she graduated from the university, Willa Cather worked as an editor in Pittsburgh and New York; but she continued to publish stories. At first they were sad and bitter, for she recalled most vividly the hardships of people she had known. Later, she wrote about musicians and artists in large cities.

But finally Willa Cather wrote a novel about Ne-

braska, a story that showed both the good and the bad of pioneer life. She named the book O Pioneers! It was her first great success. At last she knew what her years in Nebraska had destined her to do. She began to write one book after another. No matter what she named the town—Moonstone or Hanover or Sweet Water—it was always actually Red Cloud. Her storybook streets and houses were filled with people she knew. My Antonia was really her beloved Annie Sadilek; A Lost Lady was Mrs. Garber. Old Mrs. Harris, a short story, showed Grandma Boak as she lived and worked in the little house on Cedar Street. And peopling her books were other friends and acquaintances like the Miners, Mrs. Weiner, Dr. McKeeby, and Professor Shindelmeisser. Margie Anderson came to life in three of her works, always under different names. Coloring everything she wrote was her great love of the country itself—its blistering heat and bitter cold, the red grass and the flowers that were still fresh in her memory thirty years later.

When at last she wrote from her heart about the town that she once wanted to get away from, she achieved a success that no one—surely not Willa Cather herself—had ever dreamed possible.

SOURCES

There have been published numerous studies of Willa Cather, both books and articles. Some of these are concerned with analyses of her novels and short stories. For biographical purposes, however, I found four books of particular interest:

Willa Cather: A Critical Biography by Professor E. K. Brown, Alfred A. Knopf, Inc., New York, 1953.

Willa Cather Living by Edith Lewis, Alfred A. Knopf, Inc., New York, 1953.

Willa Cather, A Memoir by Elizabeth Shepley Sargeant, J. B. Lippincott Company, Philadelphia, 1953.

The World of Willa Cather by Mildred R. Bennett, Dodd, Mead and Company, New York, 1951.

Probably the most reliable sources of information about Willa Cather's Nebraska, and about her attitude toward it, are her own works, especially the novels *O Pioneers!*, *Song of the Lark*, *My Antonia*, and *A Lost Lady*. Also revealing are the collections of short stories: *Obscure Destinies*, *Five Stories by Willa Cather*, and *Early Stories of Willa Cather*.

Before Miss Cather's death in 1947, it was generally believed that she was born in 1876. Encyclopedias and biographical dictionaries accepted that date; 1876 was engraved on her tombstone in East Jaffrey, New Hampshire.

But, in the last decade, scholarship has determined an earlier date to be correct. There was no official record of her birth in Virginia; but a letter sent by her father to her uncle, George Cather, in Nebraska tells of her birth on December 7, 1873.

R. F.

ABOUT THE AUTHOR

Ruth Franchere has always had a special interest in Willa Cather as a writer. "Perhaps," she says, "I had a strong feeling of kinship for her because I spent many childhood vacations in Nebraska, visiting my grandparents. One cannot easily forget the dry heat and steady wind that are peculiar to the Cather country."

With the exception of her Nebraska vacations, the author lived in Waterloo, Iowa, until her marriage. She was graduated from the University of Iowa and then spent some years in Illinois and California. Now she makes her home in Oregon, where her husband heads the Division of Humanities at Portland State College. Mrs. Franchere has taught English composition at the University of Washington, University of Oregon, and Portland State College. She lives with her family in a delightful lake community, just a few hours from both the mountains and the sea. She has one daughter, Julie.